MAKING TRACKS

by
J.R. Fairman

Published by
Kingfisher Railway Productions
65A The Avenue, Southampton, Hampshire

Aerial view of Works about 1935 looking north-west. Log timber-pond in foreground. Main line from Southampton to Dorchester across width of picture and the Romsey line curving from Redbridge Jnc, under the road bridge across the Causeway. The long white building, centre, is the creosoting plant. The extensive sleeper stacks and the gantry crane are clearly seen. *British Rail*

Introduction

Perhaps, when we are near the railway, it is inevitable that the glamour of the locomotives and rolling stock commands our immediate attention. They are our means of travel. Their movement, power, comfort and colour ensure that they enjoy much of the publicity, official and unofficial, about the 'iron road'.

But the shining steel rails, stretching away to the distance, linking city and country, factory and mine, may conjure in our minds romantic dreams of far away places, holidays by sea, visits to or by relations, times good and times bad. For many, the nostalgia is particularly strong at dusk when the rails gleam under the early evening lights!

Probably, when we do think about the track, our minds turn to the vast engineering work involved. The cuttings, embankments, and viaducts, and the colossal task of track maintenance, ballast cleaning, bridge renewals, drainage, and the multitude of other civil engineering work that we may see taking place, especially at weekends, impress us. We cannot but admire the expertise of those engaged on these essential duties although we may also occasionally rue the delays and diversions to our train. We certainly respect the quality of the permanent way for it guarantees our safety.

Who of us gives a thought to the men and women who actually make the track? Not many!

This book is to pay tribute to those who have worked at the Redbridge Works, near Southampton, producing sleepers, rail fastenings, track sections, switches and crossings, purpose made timbers and long welded rail for others to lay on the ballast. The Works was originated by the former London and South Western Railway in 1879. It closed in 1989. For over a century it supplied the materials for those whose job it was to lay the track. The work carried out at Redbridge was vital and it is hoped the part played by the Works will be interesting to everyone using the railway.

When the site was opened it was at a time of significant railway development at Redbridge. A new viaduct was planned, to be built to carry the Southampton and Dorchester line across the River Test to replace the original structure of 1847. At the same date, 1880, the decision was taken by the Board to acquire Redbridge wharf and adjacent property, previously leased. The cost to the Company of using Eling wharf, on the west side of the estuary of the River Test, for unloading railway materials brought in by sea was considerable and it was believed it could be reduced by using the quay and under-used wharf at Redbridge, adjacent to the railway. So the L&SWR first leased the wharf in 1879 and carried out the discharge of vessels by direct labour, at the same time they used the adjacent land for storage of materials, particularly imported timber sleepers.

Within a few months the anticipated reduction of costs was being warmly welcomed by the Board and arrangements were soon made to establish ponds for seasoning timber, tanks for creosoting sleepers and facilities for fitting sleepers with chairs. The site was developed quite quickly and, in addition to chaired sleepers, switches and crossings were assembled. Throughout the years, improvements in handling and storage were introduced; but in 1923 there were a number of major developments at the Works including the installation of a pressure creosoting plant.

The wharf frontage on the Redbridge Channel was reconstructed at this time and methods of cargo handling, stacking and transport within the works were further improved. The years of the Second War gave Redbridge problems from German air attacks which led to changes in policy of storing inflammable sleepers but the most significant developments in the history of track production at Redbridge Works took place in the post-war years and were the direct outcome of alterations to track design.

In Chapter 4 the fascinating history of railway track and its components is explained and the story is taken to the present day. Fortunately, Redbridge Works was progressively modernised by British Rail to produce modern track. Timber sleepers have been supplanted by pre-stressed concrete, except for some use of hardwood, principally for crossings timbers. Rail joints connected by bolted fishplates have been replaced by long welded rail on plain track and baseplates and clips have replaced traditional chairs, screws and keys.

Redbridge's story is important because it was the last British Rail permanent way works in this country capable of making track. Only Baileyfield, in Scotland is left as a manufacturing works. It carried on the traditional self-sufficiency practiced by almost all the railway companies in the pre-Nationalisation era. In recent years its output has been used at many locations, often far from the Southern, and its quality of work and ability to make special track at short notice earned the staff at Redbridge a fine reputation.

Sadly, British Rail policy has changed and privately owned works are being used to make track, a job Redbridge did so well. The works site is, of course, very valuable but, after 3rd March 1989, Redbridge is closed. By this book, it is hoped to record for posterity its contribution to 'making track' for over 100 years.

Contents

Chapter One

The Story of Redbridge

What was Redbridge like when the railway came in 1847? A brief background history of the village will set the scene for the opening of the Works over a century ago and remind the reader that every place of work is about people and their families.

Redbridge is a village in the Parish of Millbrook four miles west of Southampton. Today it is well known by motorists for its busy roundabout at the end of the M271 and for the bridges and causeway on the A35 over the River Test. By the majority of rail users travelling from Southampton it is a glimpse of a rather non descript station, a railway yard and a sudden vista of the often muddy estuary of the River Test as the train slows and curves west towards the New Forest and Bournemouth or north to Romsey and Salisbury.

By Saxon times, and probably much earlier in history, there was a bridge over the River at Red Bridge and by the 11th Century

1860 and his widow, Jane, survived him until 1884. Near the end of her life the Redbridge Works site was acquired by the Railway Company. A Mrs Vaudrey, the third cousin of Sir John Barker Mill, became Lord of the Manor and later she took the name, Mrs Barker Mill and for years she held the annual court leet of the Manor of Millbrook at Redbridge, latterly at the Ship Hotel. This brief story covers the historical background to the title of the land at Redbridge.

Redbridge has long been associated with the sea. Today its past links with seafarers are to be found in the names of its two old inns, 'The Anchor' and 'The Ship'. Its position at the head of Southampton Water is shared with Eling Wharf on the west side of the estuary. Upstream the River Test is shallow and virtually impassable by any boats except those of a very shallow draft. So one can appreciate the value of Redbridge Wharf in

An engraving about 1840 looking south-east, showing the village and the old bridges (still surviving) across the River Test. A two-masted vessel is moored at the old quay. The large house on the right was then the home of the Gearing family. The Anchor Inn is above the old medieval bridge and the chimney of the Brewery behind. The ozier (reed) beds were worked commercially in those days.

there was a wharf, called 'Kings' Wharf. We know this because, in 1045, King Edward granted land at Nursling, Redbridge and Millbrook to the Bishop of Winchester. The boundary includes these words . . . . . 'thence to the weir on the River near Redbridge, out to the stream to the Kings' Wharf and so along the stream back to Redbridge and the *hedge* to Hampton.' The future Redbridge Works and much of the hinterland was a part of this large estate.

In 1545, at the troublesome times of the Reformation, the Dean and Chapter surrendered the Manor to King Henry VIII. Millbrook and Nursling were then granted to a King's man, John Mill. Centuries passed. In 1835 there was no direct heir and the estate passed to John Barker, the son of the sister of the deceased Sir Charles Mill. John assumed the name Barker-Mill, died in

serving the needs of the villages on the east side of the Test, as Eling gave similar service to those on the west. The bridge was, of course, very important. It was the only bridge downstream from Romsey and was of particular value, not only for carts, coaches and the military but also for moving animals from the country to Southampton. It was a toll bridge and the income was used for its upkeep. The bridge was damaged in the Civil War and in the latter part of the 17th Century a new stone causeway bridge was built over the main channel comprising five spans with round arches, on the site of the earlier bridge. It can still be seen today and is an interesting survivor of a medieval design, built of ashlar and rubble and having prominent cut-waters carried up to the parapet on the seaward side. The old bridge over the Western Channel has a single 57ft 6in span.

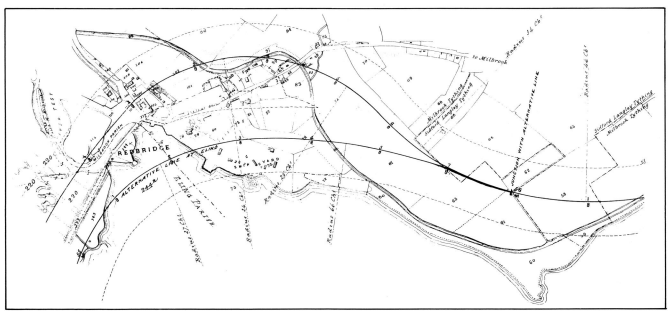

Plan of Redbridge, Southampton & Dorsetshire Railway, 1844 showing alternative routes through the village. The southerly route near the water was chosen.

In 1926-30, after years of planning, new reinforced concrete bridges and a causeway were built parallel with the old bridges, on their south side. The north part of the old village street of Redbridge, for so many centuries the main road between Southampton and the west, was demolished for the abutments of the arch over the street itself. The old road through the village, once choked with traffic, was bypassed and Redbridge became a quiet backwater dominated by the gloomy concrete spans overhead. After another 40 years a parallel bridge to create a dual carriageway was added. Yet, despite these and other intrusive developments like the 1966 15-storey Redbridge Towers flats, there is still some character in the village. Perhaps a description given by a visitor in 1888 will conjure a little of its past. 'Redbridge is a pretty little village with seafaring charm at every cottage door. Many houses have parrots in cages hanging at their thresholds. Men all wear dark blue jerseys. Only the stench of the Fertiliser Works wafting across the River from Eling spoils the good impression of the pleasant spot.'!

Transport, other than by road or sea, came to Redbridge at an early date. In 1770 a survey was made for a Canal from the village up the Test valley to Andover. The economic justification for the project was based on carrying coal and building materials from Southampton through Redbridge to Romsey, Stockbridge and Andover and returning with agricultural produce, in particular, corn. In 1789 the Act of Parliament authorising the 22 miles long Canal was passed, construction followed, and it was opened for business about 1796. The Canal Wharf and lock at Redbridge was built just north of the River bridge, on the east bank, within a short distance of Redbridge Wharf. Barges were able to work through from the Canal to Southampton or transhipment could take place from sea going ships at Redbridge. No traces of the Canal at Redbridge have survived, although a brick wall parallel with the railway to Romsey marks the boundary.

Another scheme for a Canal was surveyed in 1792. This was the Salisbury and Southampton Canal which was projected to use the Andover Canal from Romsey nearly as far as the Wharf and sea-lock at Redbridge. From Redbridge to Southampton the proposed route branched off the original Andover Canal 150 yards north of the Wharf and then passed round the north and east sides of the village. It then ran parallel with the shore of the upper reaches of Southampton Water to Blechynden, whence a 880 yard

long tunnel was planned and built under the town to take the Canal to the River Itchen at Northam and to Southampton quay. The Act was passed in 1795 but construction was slow and it was the end of 1802 before the Canal was opened between Redbridge and the west end of Southampton tunnel. However, problems with financing the completion of the Canal at both the Salisbury and the Southampton ends led to its early demise. The sparce traffic on the section round Redbridge only lasted in fact for only four years.

But the Andover Canal survived well into the Railway era. In the 1840's there were sixteen 18-ton barges at work and Mr R Sharp was the agent at Redbridge. It did not, however, have a future because it followed a route down the valley to the coast that was considered eminently suitable for projected north-south railway schemes and in 1846 the ambitiously named Manchester and Southampton Railway agreed to buy the Canal Company for £30,000. Of this more anon.

The first railway actually surveyed to pass through Redbridge was the Southampton and Dorsetshire Railway via Rimpton (as stated on the plans) in 1844. Captain W. Moorsom, Esq., was the engineer and the statutory documents were deposited with Parliament and with the County authority on 30th November of that year. Alternative routes through the village were shown on the Plan.

A year earlier, dated 4th March, 1843, a Tithe Map of the Parish of Millbrook had been prepared, the survey being pursuant to the Act for the Commutation of Tithes in England and Wales. Fortunately this shows the shipyard and wharves at Redbridge as they existed in pre-railway days. Shipbuilding at Redbridge had been long established and there are records of 'a good dock where the best ships are built', in 1600. In the latter part of the 18th century several small naval vessels were built at Redbridge. Two, called the 'Redbridge' and the 'Millbrook' were each about 150 tons and one carried sixteen and one fourteen guns. Two others, called the 'Dart' and the 'Arrow' were each 600 tons burthen and each carried 28 32-pounders. In the mid-1840's David Purkis was listed in the Directory as a shipbuilder and Abraham Purkis was the wharfinger who leased the wharf near the Bridge from Sir John Barker Mill, the Lord of the Manor and landowner.

The village was also the home of a number of Master Mariners; for example, in 1845, James Penny and William

Alexander are named. Isaac Purkis was the riverpilot in 1839 and was succeeded by his son, James, in 1843 while G. Williams was the resident Officer of Excise. The existence of this post indicates that foreign trade was significant. In 1843 the lessee of the river frontage, the marsh and timber yard, (which was destined to become a part of Redbridge Works) was Walter Morrice but in the following year William Row Sharland, who had been the tanner at Tanners Brook, took over the lease. Benjamin Self was landlord of the Anchor Inn and Fred Groombridge was mine host at the Ship Inn. There were the usual shops and trades; a grocer and post office (last post 8.45pm!), coal merchant, bricklayer; perhaps 70 houses in all. The only other business of importance was Richard Stride's brewery. That was the village, until the railway came.

The Southampton and Dorchester Railway Act was passed by Parliament on 21st July, 1845 and the contract for its construction was awarded to a large and reputable firm, Messrs Grissell and Peto. Although the land purchased by the railway and many earthworks and structures were wide enough for double track, only the first four miles, from Southampton to Redbridge, were actually laid in 1846/7 with a double line of rails. For much of this section the filled-in bed of the Salisbury and Southampton Canal was used. The chosen route through Redbridge was to the south of the village street. Access to Sharland's timber yard was given by an occupation crossing just west of the station and the bed of the disused Canal was bridged by the railway at the east end. The choice of Redbridge and not Totton for a station on

Tranquility on the river. Perhaps the sailing barge is bringing timber up to Redbridge quay.   *British Rail*

the Dorchester railway shows the relative traffic expectations from the villages at that time. At Totton only a simple platform was provided on Junction Road before the present Totton station was opened in 1859. The embankment approach to the timber viaduct built across the River Test covered much of the site of the old Redbridge quay.

Public services, five trains each way on weekdays, four on Sundays, started on 1st June, 1847 and traffic developed satisfactorily. In 1848 the S&DR was amalgamated with the London & South Western Railway which had worked its trains from the outset. In 1857/8, the line was doubled from Redbridge over the viaduct and on to Ringwood and Wimborne.

Redbridge's first station master in 1847 was Mr A. Martin and his new home was the present station house adjoining the up platform. He must have been a close neighbour with Mr Sharland who had plans to develop his yard and timber business at the old shipyard and wharf. He must also have had many discussions with Mr Sharp, the canal agent, in regard to proposals being made for a railway over the Andover to Redbridge Canal.

In 1850, Mr Sharp would have learnt that the Canal was to be closed as soon as the L&SWR and M&SR had handed over the purchase money. This transaction did not take place but, from 1854, the Canal Company was forced to reduce its rates for the carriage of goods because the L&SWR had opened a new railway from Basingstoke to Andover and were undercutting the charges made by the Canal. Steady business continued on the Canal. In 1856 Mr Sharp left and was replaced by Edmund Skeats who was, within four years to witness the end of the Canal era at Redbridge.

In 1857, the Great Western Railway approached the Canal Company with a proposal to lay a broad gauge railway over the Canal bed to Redbridge as a part of their proposed extension from Salisbury to Southampton. This project was not accepted by Parliament but the Canal Company themselves then decided it would be sound economic sense to promote their own railway, and the Andover Canal Railway Act was duly passed. Probably it had the backing of the Great Western. The discussions between the GWR and the L&SWR as to who should acquire the Andover and Redbridge are too complex to be included in the story of Redbridge itself. Suffice it to say that the L&SWR won the day, paid £12,500 in cash and a similar sum in £10 shares and the Canal was finally shut in the autumn of 1859. Mr Skeats continued to live at Redbridge until 1865 and was in business as a coal agent until the railway was opened from Romsey by the L&SWR as a single line on 6th March, 1865 to the present location of the junction between the station and the viaduct.

At Eling Wharf on the west side of the river estuary, the Southampton and Dorchester Railway had, in 1851, built a short branch line from Totton to the Quay. It had been authorised by Act of Parliament on 2nd July, 1847 and was leased to the owner of the quay, Sir John Barker Mill. It opened, for goods traffic only, and is still in use in 1989, although not as far as the quay itself. Before they acquired Redbridge, the L&SWR used Eling for receiving supplies of softwood railway sleepers, also as a delivery point for rails, fishplates and castings. Burt Boulton and Haywoods were established timber importers and, for example, in 1877, were awarded a contract for 280,000 Baltic pine sleepers at 3/1½d (16p!) each, for discharge at Eling. There also, the Rhymney Iron Co. delivered 200 tons of iron fishplates at £5. 16. 0 a ton, the West Cumberland Iron and Steel Co. 1500 tons of rail at £5 19. 6 a ton and the Anderston Foundry Co. 2000 tons of cast iron chairs at £3. 5. 7 a ton.

This was the transport scene when the Redbridge Works was 'born'. No doubt many of the local residents were horrified at all the changes taking place!

Chapter Two

The Birth of the Works

The end of the 1870's found Redbridge on the verge of major changes affecting the village and the railway. There were strong rumours about a Southampton and Isle of Wight Junction Railway scheme for a second line across the river, from the Andover branch to Totton thence south by a tunnel under the Solent to Gurnet Bay to join the Newport and Cowes Railway. There were also plans to double the track of the single line railway between Romsey and Redbridge. Even more important there was a proposal to replace the 1847 timber viaduct on the Dorchester line with a new iron structure.

The Isle of Wight railway scheme, subject of a letter from J.E. Barnes to the L&SWR in May, 1880 was considered by the Directors but they declined to support it and informed Mr Barnes accordingly.

The viaduct renewal was a more complex proposition the new bridge had to be built while the old remained in use. The old Southampton & Dorchester Railway timber viaduct was 371 yards long and consisted of 48 spans varying from 23ft to 27ft, the height of the openings being 6ft above high water O.S tide and 17ft above the bed of the river. The new bridge was to be 215 yards long, consisting of 30 spans of 20ft each and a height of 4ft above high water mark.

A deviation was needed to build the new bridge while trains continued over the old. Therefore, Parliamentary powers were needed to acquire an additional strip of Southampton Water and the bed of the River Test. By the same Act, the L&SWR applied for powers to purchase all the land of Redbridge Wharf, the timber yard, sawpits, sheds, landing stage, the mudlands and the

An 'up' stopping train from Bournemouth enters Redbridge station about 1910, headed by an Adams 7ft express locomotive No. 683.

Willstead

The widening of the 5¼ miles of track to Romsey was approved and contracts were awarded to Messrs Perry and Firbank. Work proceeded in 1883 and the Board of Trade Inspecting Officer, Colonel Rich made his inspection of the completed work on 25th February, 1884. The 1865 crossing of the main road to the Bridges opposite the Anchor Inn was passed by the Inspector, including the signal box, called Test Gates, where 'gates were interlocked with signals worked from a raised cabin'. It must be admitted that the train service, six trains on weekdays between Andover and Southampton, hardly appeared to justify the provision of a double line of rails but the doubling must have been carried out in anticipation of increased traffic from a new railway from Swindon opened through to Andover in 1883. In those days all Salisbury trains from Southampton went via Bishopstoke (Eastleigh) and Chandler's Ford.

dock, stores and offices and the occupation road leading across the railway to the premises. These were applied for in the L&SWR Company's Bill in November 1880, and granted by Parliament in 1881.

On 11th November 1880 the Common Seal of the Company was affixed to a deed assigning from William Row Sharland to the L&SWR the freehold of the wharf premises previously leased from him by the Company. The precise date of the first lease taken on the Redbridge site is not known but it was probably earlier in 1880 because, in the previous year, 1879, rail, chairs and sleepers were still being delivered to Eling. It is very likely that the land was also envisaged as a useful site for receiving and storing materials for the new viaduct and for the widening of the railway to Romsey.

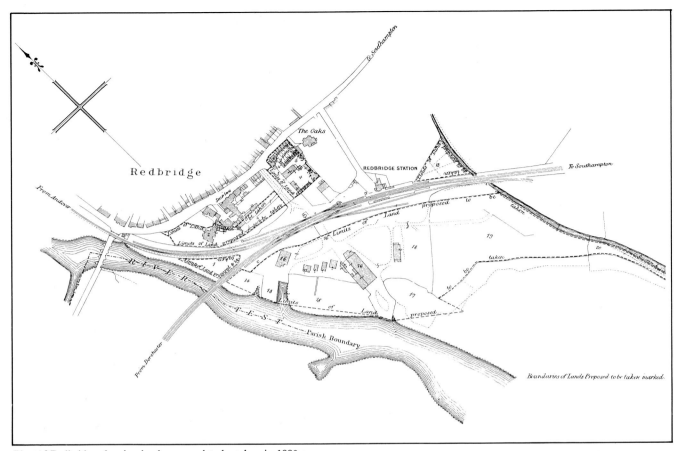

Plan of Redbridge showing land proposed to be taken in 1880.

On 24th November 1881 the L&SWR made an agreement with the owners of the land, the trustees of aged Dame Jane Barker Mill, in respect of their property at Redbridge. This approved plans for the enlargement and development of the wharves there. Within a month, the Railway Company were stipulating to the Ebbw Vale Co. Ltd that steel rail and to Anderston Foundry Co. that chairs should be delivered to Redbridge and not to Eling. Additional sidings at Redbridge were approved by the L&SWR Traffic Committee in May 1882 probably for contractor's use because it was agreed that the materials used would be returned to the Company when no longer required. Henry Sims, the Station master, also had a new office erected for his use early in 1882, and later in the same year plans were prepared for increasing the passenger accommodation at an estimated cost of £1091, a lot of money in those days. In May, 1883 an extension and alterations was approved for the station sidings at an estimated cost of £378. The importance of the railway to Redbridge was growing rapidly!

The arrangements made by the L&SWR for discharging, storing and handling railway materials at Eling had been carried on for many years with a tenant or lessee who was under agreement with the wharf owner, Sir John Barker Mill. In 1881 the lessee was Mr Fletcher. In 1883 there were questions about the Company's rights on their use of the sidings to the wharf, also their authority for storing materials there. The Company's solicitors and those of Mrs Vaudrey, the heir to the Mill estate, came to satisfactory arrangements in these matters but the charges made by Mr Fletcher compared most unfavourably with the costs of direct landing at Redbridge Wharf. At the end of 1882 the

use of Redbridge had saved £2660 in one year compared with Mr Fletcher's charges and the former arrangements at Eling Wharf. In 1883 £4398 was saved. The railway's Engineering Committee expressed themselves as 'well satisfied'. The tenancy of the wharf at Eling was expected to be available for purchase during 1883 but the L&SWR were happy with Redbridge and decided not to pursue the matter.

The Company were now determined to develop their Redbridge yard as a depot and they acted with commendable speed. Open clay-lined creosote tanks for preserving imported softwood sleepers were built in 1882 and in July 1883 approval was given to roofing over the tanks also the area used for chairing sleepers. By the end of 1883 plans had been prepared for the erection of a new steam travelling crane, the improvement of the wharf by dredging alongside the old piles, for the provision of new connections between sidings and for the repair and strengthening of the facings of the upper quay.

In July, 1884, additional freehold land, previously leased was purchased for £1200 from the Barker Mill estate and in November of that year a dredging was bought from a Mr Gannaway of Southampton for £150 for use at Redbridge and other places, like Lymington. It started operating at Redbridge in the following summer.

Meanwhile the work of piling and erecting the new iron viaduct across the River Test had continued during 1882/3. The Company's seal was affixed to the conveyance from the Board of Trade to the L&SWR of that part of the bed of the River Test 'shown on the plan', for a nominal yearly rent of one shilling! An amusing sequel to this purchase was the discovery by the

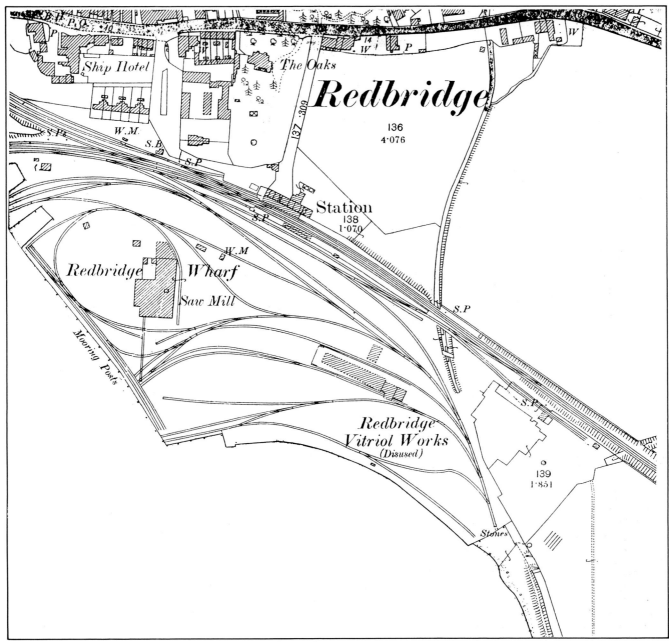

25 ins OS map of Redbridge Yard. 1895 revision of 1867 survey.

L&SWR that they had re-purchased a strip of the river bed which they already owned! On 6th June, 1883 the completed structure, which was just to the south of the old timber viaduct, was passed by the Board of Trade and the Inspecting Officer and opened for traffic. The only subsequent additions were timber fenders and dolphins to protect the piers and their provision was approved by the Harbour Department of the Board of Trade at the end of August. History was repeated 80 years later when the 1883 viaduct was replaced by the present piled reinforced concrete structure, opened on 31st May, 1964 and using the line of the 1847 railway. This recent structure has two bridges, one over the Redbridge Channel and one over the River Test and the bridges are separated by a man made island or stone-faced earth embankment.

To supervise the Depot, the L&SWR appointed a Superintendent of Stores, William Arthur Bailey. He was the 'father' of Redbridge Works and was in charge for ten years until succeeded by Mr McCarraher. The Superintendent's home was quite a large house in the village called 'The Chestnuts'. It still stands in 1989 at the corner of Tate Road leading to the works. Redbridge's population, in 1883, was becoming quite railway orientated. As well as Mr Bailey and the stationmaster, Mr Barnes (who continued in service until 1892), there were three signalmen, Walter Chambers, John Martin and Fred Batten; a porter, Alf Wolvin; a ganger, Bill Brewer; two warehousemen, John Colson and Henry Penny; and a watchman, Stephen Pentham. Working at Redbridge must have been thirst provoking because, in addition to the 'Anchor' and the 'Ship' (Hotel), there were two more Inns;

The former Dixon & Cardus Linseed Oil and Oil Cake Mills, south east corner, January, 1924. Note the Fire Alarm bell on the post.
Demolition of the Oil Cake Mills in June 1924. Latterly it was used by the railway as a Saw Mill. The newly built office and stores are on the left.
British Rail

A view in June 1924, looking west, showing the new machine shop under construction. The 'B4' class 0-4-0T is shunting on the quay. In the top right corner is the steam pump house, later the shunting engine shed.

British Rail

the 'Flag of Liberty' and the 'Wool Pack' and Strides brewery had become known as the Redbridge Brewery and its owner was listed as a licensed brewer, maltser and brandy merchant! Mr Stride's home was 'The Oaks' but he died in 1887 and the Brewery was closed.

The story of the Redbridge Works would be incomplete without recording other industrial activities on the site than shipbuilding. Both were concerned with agriculture, one for cattle feed and fertilisers and the other for the production of manures. The first works was the South Western oil mills, established in 1849 by W.G. Ashby. In 1853 Cecil Dixon and John Cardus established the Dixon & Cardus Oil and Cake Mills, seed crushers and stores. This firm also had a factory at Southampton, near Northam bridge, and in 1899, after 50 years at Redbridge they decided to close the premises and concentrate production at Northam where they were active until the last war. The principal building of the oil mills was about 100ft x 150ft and was 200ft inside the site entrance (the present level crossing). The L&SWR adapted it as a Saw Mill when it became vacant.

Another Works was built in 1897/8 and this was on 'green field' site east of the disused Canal. It was for the Schultz Gunpowder Co and was approved by the L&SWR in October, 1900, Mr W Clay was the man first in charge. The powder works were active for 23 years and during its life was extended to occupy a triangular plot of nearly 7½ acres, served by a siding off the main line. The area was, in later years, the Works foundry, pattern shop and storage yard for castings. Because Mr Schultz was an alien, his Works was taken over by the Navy in 1914 and Mr W. Robertson was appointed to manage the production of gun cotton. Two of the additional First War buildings added by the Navy survived in 1988. The gunpowder works closed in 1922 but 60 years later at least one local ex-employee could remember her time there; she lost the tip of her finger when there was an explosion! The Southern Railway purchased the site of the powder works in 1926. At the east end of the powder works there stood a large bungalow for the manager. Appropriately it was called 'The

Bungalow'. Access was across the railway from a footpath across the fields from the main road. It was pulled down in 1961. The Works chimney, a well-known landmark in Redbridge was felled on 14th July, 1927 when the site was being prepared for the future railway foundry.

In 1935, at the west end of the Schultz site a small asphalt and bitumen blending works was established by Scientific Roads, (Southern), Ltd and continued there until about 1948 when the trading name was the Alexander Asphalt Co. Ltd. There was a siding connection for bitumen tank wagons parallel with the main line and one of the 1914 powder factory Naval buildings was used as the office. There was also a small boiler plant. Forty years later, on a hot day, the unwary walker can find tangible evidence of the former occupants and their business!

Finally in this history of the site, reference must be made to the Vitriol works started in 1863 by Alfred Lock. It was later served by a siding. In 1883 the works was developed with a new ammonia distillation plant by Mr Lock and a partner, Mr Finch and it was operated by Messrs A.W. Hall and Co. About 1887 it was owned by the Empire Chemical Co. who were advertising products from their Redbridge Works; lime, and artificial manures, particularly sulphate of ammonia. Hugh Hudson was their manager from 1887 but the Works appears to have closed down in 1892 with Joe Ody was the last man in charge. The buildings forming the Vitriol works were on the site that became the creosoting plant.

In addition to these manufacturing concerns, William Sharland, the lessee of the wharf from 1844 had continued after the railway was built, with his son, also named William, in the family business as a timber merchant and they developed further interests with a corn and coal yard. They lived and had their office in Ivy House, still standing on the corner of Old Redbridge Road adjacent to the Ship Inn yard. Once the L&SWR had established their depot at Redbridge in 1880 and acquired the premises formerly occupied by the firm, Sharland & Co, appears to have ceased trading about 1883.

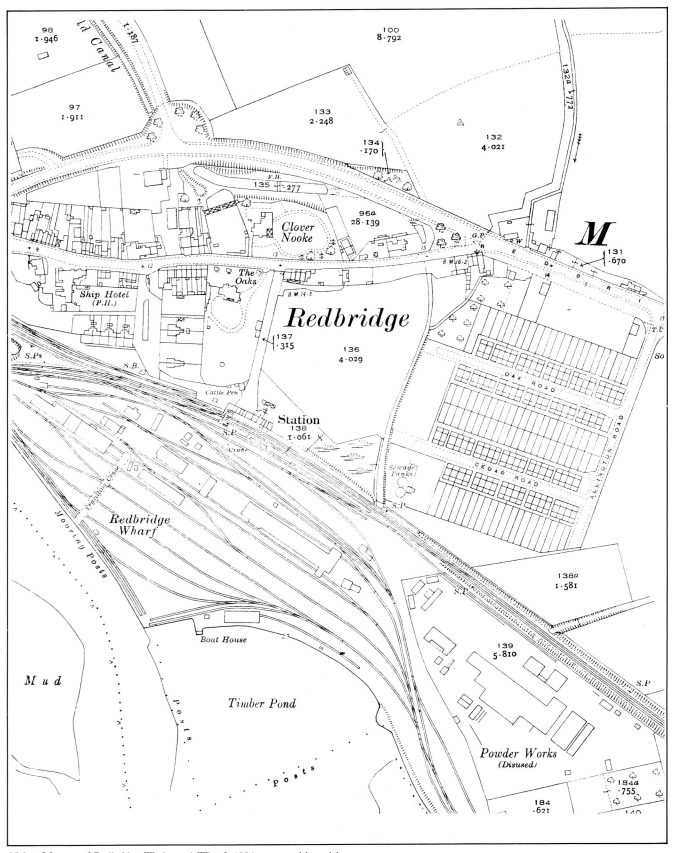

25 ins OS map of Redbridge Works and Wharf. 1926 survey with revisions.

Chapter Three
Railway Track
The Story of its Development

In the Introduction to this book the role of Redbridge Works in making railway track was briefly explained. Rail and sleepers, points and crossings are well known terms and understood by every user of the railway but fewer travellers will have noticed how many different types of track components there are, even on the tracks of modern British Rail.

The reader with an inquisitive mind will want to know more! Look at the illustrations and spot the differences. Then, on your next visit to a station see how many variations you can

'spot'. Here's a tip! A good place to find older and unusual track is in sidings or near buffer stops.

First, let us have a short history lesson; the fascinating story of the development of railway track from the earliest waggon-ways to today's high speed rail routes.

It is usually accepted that the true origin of 'rail-ways', as parallel lines of 'rail' to carry and guide waggons can be traced back to the 16th century in Germany, in mines. By the closing years of that century, it is recorded that 'rails' were in use for

Cannon Street, 19th June, 1926. The complexity of the old style layout can be judged from this picture of the London terminus in pre-electrification days.

British Rail

Left: Bull-head rail and a steel sleeper with chairs cast integral. These were used in large numbers on the Great Western Railway. Beyond are examples of tied and untied concrete pot sleepers.

Centre left: In a siding are three pairs of tied pot sleepers of 1940's design that returned to the stone blocks of the 1830's!

Centre right: A comparison between standard 4ft 8in gauge and Brunel's GWR 7ft 0¼in broad gauge, the latter laid on longitudinal sleepers with ties to maintain gauge.

Left: A concrete sleeper with cast iron chairs secured by bolts nutted at the top. Redbridge had a production line to chair such sleepers in the 1950's. Beyond are timber sleepers with spiked baseplates for flat bottom rail and a modern prestressed Dow-Mac concrete sleeper.
All photos, John Fairman

waggon haulage at coal pits in Nottinghamshire. Throughout the 17th and 18th centuries rail waggon-ways were introduced to facilitate the movement of coal from pits to loading points on rivers or canals in Co. Durham, Northumberland, on Tyneside and elsewhere. Horses could pull much heavier loads with the waggon wheels running on a hard surface. Early rails were usually made of oak and it is known that New Forest oak was shipped north for this purpose, perhaps from Eling, as return loads on collier brigs.

From about 1716 wrought iron strips were first added to the surface of rails on curves to reduce wear on the oak, and cast-iron plates were similarly used from 1738. Abraham Darby's foundry at Coalbrookdale, Shropshire, produced cast-iron rails in short lengths experimentally in 1767, and, being successful and much more durable than timber rails this material was widely adopted by the end of the century in place of timber for rails on wagon-ways.

One problem with the early cast-iron rails was the ease with which this material fractures under bending load. Adequate support was necessary to reduce the frequency of breakage and stone blocks to give a good foundation were introduced in 1790 by the Butterfly Iron Co., Derbyshire, while the first chair was used in 1797 at Newcastle. The chair formed a cradle to carry the rail and it rested on the stone block.

Up to 1789 all the early railways used rails with vertical sides to guide flat tyred wagon wheels. The National Railway Museum at York has a good exhibit showing this type of plateway. It was William Jessop who pioneered the first use of a flanged wheel to run on his design of 3ft long cast-iron edge rails. For 20 years some wagonways used the plateway and some adopted the new edge rail. This was the dawn of the railway era. In the south the first public railway promoted independently of a canal was sanctioned by Parliament in 1801. This was Jessop's Surrey Iron Railway, from Wandsworth to Croydon. In the north the first Iron Railway was laid down in 1797 from the Walker Colliery to the Tyne.

So, by the turn of the 18th/19th century the true genesis of the accepted format of railway track had arrived and the old waggon-way was progressively displaced by the flanged wheel on the edge rail. The brittle nature of cast-iron has already been mentioned. The more suitable and tougher malleable wrought iron rail in square or rectangular section was introduced from 1805 and by 1811 was available in about 15ft lengths. A more economical T-section was introduced and this was followed by a much improved fish-bellied longitudinal section, weighing about 33lb/yard, patented by John Birkenshaw of the Bedlington Ironworks in 1820. This was the design used for the Stockton & Darlington and was chosen by George Stephenson for the Liverpool and Manchester Railway in 1829. He used rails in 15ft lengths, 35 lb/yard, laid on solid stone blocks or on half-round oak or larch sleepers.

By 1837 further progress was made in the design of rail and Joseph Locke introduced the double headed wrought iron rail for the Grand Junction Railway built between Birmingham and Warrington. The idea was to turn the rail every few years and equalise the wear on both surfaces. These rails were laid in cast-iron chairs with wooden keys to wedge the rails in the chairs. Unfortunately the idea of turning the rails over did not work in practice because the rail head became damaged in contact with the chairs, also the running surface work-hardened.

Through the 1840's the weight of rail being used on the new lines was quickly increased to cater for heavier locomotives and carriages and higher speeds. The double headed rail section gave way to the 'bull-head' section on which the upper part was heavier than the lower but this new section was not, of course,

reversible. So, from the 35lb/yard wrought-iron rails used on the L&MR in 1829, 80lb/yard double headed rails were in use by 1850 and bull head rails of up to 85 lb/yard by the mid-'seventies.

The lengths of rail in use were also soon increased, from 15ft to 20ft in 1850 and 24ft, for example on the new Settle and Carlisle Railway in 1875. The first steel rails produced by the Bessemer process were used experimentally in 1857 and major trials were carried out on the London and North Western Railway in 1862. Steel showed great advantages over wrought iron and within a few years was the standard metal specified. The durability of steel and the ability to roll longer lengths of rail compared with wrought iron, also developments in handling techniques, made it possible, for example, for the London and South Western Railway to standardise on 45ft lengths of steel rail by 1880 when Redbridge was opened.

Only the Great Western Railway differed from the general development of the standard of 4ft 8½in gauge, railways. The GWR was laid by Brunel to the broad 7ft 0¼in gauge and at first used a bridge section rail, 44 to 62 lb/yard. By 1877 they had 1684 miles of bridge rail still in use, 1215 miles with double headed rail, 289 miles of Vignoles rail, (a flat bottomed section), and only 30 miles of bull headed rail. Only after the abolition of the broad gauge in 1892 did the GWR come completely into the accepted practice of using steel bull headed rail.

In 1904/5 a Committee of senior officers of a number of major railway companies, including the GWR and LNWR, met with the object of designing a British standard rail to replace the many individual designs of bull head rail used by the various companies. The result was a British Standard Specification 95 lb/yard section which was adopted and used for nearly half a century, also similar 85 lb/yard sections for subsidiary or branch lines and 100 lb/yard for heavier duties. One great advantage of the standardisation was that the design of fishplates, the bolted links joining consecutive lengths of rail, were uniform for all three weights of rail.

An alternative section, the flat bottom rail, was not introduced as a British Railway standard until 1949. This section had been adopted by almost all overseas railways, also for some industrial railways, military railways and light railways in this country. In its cheapest form the rails were held in position on the timber sleepers by spikes. Later, sole plates between the rail and sleepers were introduced and these reduced the tendency for rails to 'creep' and reduced sleeper wear. In Britain the distinctive practice continued of using bull head rail kept securely in position by wooden keys in heavy cast iron chairs which were securely fixed to timber sleepers by spikes and trenails, fang bolts or steel screws.

In 1936 experiments were started by the London Midland and Scottish Railway using flat bottom rail on test stretches of track. Two years later the London and North Eastern Railway followed suit and in the 1940's FB rail started to take over from the traditional bull head section. In 1949 two new designs of flat bottom rail were standardised by British Railways. They were the 109 lb/yard and 98 lb/yard sections and these designs were supplemented in 1959 by British Standard Specifications for weights between 60 lb and 110 lb/yard.

Today the BR standard rail for main lines use is 113 lb/yard. The lengths, up to 120ft, are rolled at the British Steel mills at Workington, Cumbria by the continuous casting process involving pouring up to 400 tons of molten steel without stopping into a mould to produce a continuous billet at the far end of the process. As the billet emerges, it is cut into the normal length ingot, after which the usual rolling process follows.

All sections of rail require secure support so that the load of the train is transferred to the sleepers, thence to the track bed.

Cast-iron chairs adopted in the earliest days of the railway became the standard method of supporting rails on sleepers in our perculiarly British design of permanent way. Rails are held firmly in the chairs by wedges or keys and the design of the 'jaw' of chairs between which the rail fits, ensures that the rail is at an angle of 20° to the vertical, leaning inwards. With corresponding wheel profile, this ensures smooth riding of carriages and wagons.

The early stone blocks to support chairs were displaced entirely soon after 1840 and timber became standard material for the chaired sleeper rail-road. The usual timber for sleepers in Britain was imported Baltic Redwood, or Douglas Fir, both softwoods. In more recent years imports have also been from further afield, particularly Canadian Douglas Fir and French Maritime Pine. 10in wide by 5in thick or 12in wide for joint sleepers are the usual section and they are laid transversely about 3ft apart except at the rail joints where they are sometimes 2ft apart. Hardwood would be preferable to softwood but, except for special locations it was prohibitively expensive even though its life could be up to 25 years compared with six to ten years for a pine sleeper. The designs of support for the Great Western Railway broad gauge track of the 19th century was different and is beyond the scope of this book.

The design of ordinary chairs varied considerably and there are also many patterns for different purposes. Typically, in the 1880's the standard chair weighed 40lbs each. Up to 1890, chairs had a smooth base but then the practice of making them with a serrated base was started and this helped retain the chair in its position by a better grip on the sleeper. Some railway used parallel sided wood keys and some used taper keys. The chair design was modified accordingly. A few railways preferred to have the keys inside the chair so that a man inspecting the line could see if all was secure while he patrolled along the centre line of the track. There were special chairs for sharply curving track requiring check or guard rails and these chairs had double width jaws to take the check rail as well as the running rail. Some companies used special joint-chairs with larger bases to give an increased area for carrying the ends of lengths of rail. It is at swtiches and crossings where chair design is most complex. Take a look on your next visit to a station with points and crossovers.

White or untreated timber was used for sleepers up to the end of the 1870's but the rapid decay of softwood by wet rot and

FB and bull-head rail fishplates. The BH rail chairs are standard Southern pattern for steel keys, type SI-SK. The wires connecting the rails on each side of the joint are to preserve track circuit continuity.

The skirted fishplate was introduced to give a more robust support to the joints of 95lb/yard BH rail where this type of rail had been retained after the general introduction of FB rail.

Two weights/sections of FB rail on timber sleepers using baseplates fixed inside the rails by Macbeth spike anchors and outside by galvanised screws. Note the special stepped fishplates, also the incising marks on the two left-hand fir sleepers. Oak and hemlock were also used for sleepers when redwood was scarce. *All photos, John Fairman*

Typical BH chaired rail on timber sleepers with wooden, probably oak, keys. (Teak was also used.) They were driven in the direction the rail would tend to creep in daily service. On this piece of track, the direction of travel of trains would have been predominantly from left to right. Yorkshire Dales Railway, September 1988.

Chaired, wooden keyed track of the early 20th century. This shows BH rail of the London, Brighton & South Coast Railway in chairs made in 1912 and displayed at Sheffield Park on the Bluebell Railway. The chair is fixed with two spikes and two screws. Spikes were not good fastenings as they tended to work loose in the wood.

The type SI-X chair for BH rail was used extensively by the Great Western Railway. It had two bolts up through the sleeper, nutted at the top and held from turning by a ridged head underneath. When new it was a sound design but problems of tightening arose when the sleeper rotted and the head turned. Photograph taken at Redbridge.

dry rot showed that preservative treatment was required and railway companies were surprisingly slow to introduce creosoting plant, for example on the Midland railway at Beeston by the 1880's and at Redbridge early in that decade. More details are given in Chapter 4.

Alternative materials for sleepers were tried. The pressed steel sleeper was patented by F.W. Webb on the London & North Western Railway in 1880 but in use it was found to suffer from corrosion, to cost twice that of a wooden sleeper, and to compare unfavourably in many ways with its timber counterpart. The North Eastern Railway made extensive trials in the 1900's and the Great Western Railway and other railways from the 1920's. They were marketed by GKN, Ebbw Vale, Dorman Long, Sandberg, and Workington Steelworks but problems with track circuiting and the steel shortage in the last war finally put paid to them. The steel sleepers used latterly were hot rolled and pressed trough section, 8ft 6in long, 8½in x 3in and the iron chairs were cast directly onto the plate and secured by cast rivets. Although the material was not used extensively examples can still be found by the keen 'track detective'.

Ferro-concrete sleepers were also introduced in the 1900's but found little favour. The concrete tended to disintegrate rapidly and the sleepers were very heavy to handle. The material was again of interest in the last war as a result of shortage of timber and steel. Some, made in 1940 for sidings, were simply concrete 'pots' similar to the stone blocks of 100 years before! The 'wartime' full length transverse sleepers were far from satisfactory in service on running lines where speeds are fairly high and fractured under load but the pre-stressed concrete sleeper was much more successful and its design has steadily improved. In this type the reinforcement is in the form of pre-tensioned steel wires along the length of the sleeper and this gives greatly enhanced strength to the beam. In 1964 British Rail decided that pre-stressed concrete sleepers would be standard with continuous welded rails and development work followed which has eliminated the problems associated with fastenings. In today's sleeper the metal components are cast into the concrete at manufacture and there are no longer any problems from timber or fibre inserts as used in the earlier designs.

Left: A 1921-dated chair, (although cast by SR!), on a wartime concrete pot, fixed by spikes through trenails (wooden sleeves) inserted in holes in the pot.

Above: Three chairs of London & South Western Railway design, dated 1879, 1880 and 1897.　　　　*All photos, John Fairman*

There were more than sixty patent fastenings devised for FB track. This 1958 BR2 baseplate is secured with Macbeth spike anchors to a timber sleeper. Yorkshire Dales Railway, Embsay, September 1988.

Mills C3R clips on baseplates secured with four screw fastenings onto incised fir sleepers. Templecombe, August 1988.

On the main line near Liskeard, October, 1988. Left is the Pandrol clip adopted as BR standard for FB rail on concrete sleepers in 1966. The SHC clips, centre and right, made by the Tempered Steel Co. were not suitable for third-rail electrified track because the clip was driven in sideways under the fixed bar.

An experimental length of concrete sleepers and FB rail, laid at Redbridge Works about 1950, to measure expansion and to evaluate continuous welded rail before it was introduced onto running lines. BJB clips were used with screws into fibre sleeves set into the concrete sleepers. This test length was still in place in 1989.   *All photos John Fairman*

An early design of fastening for FB rail on concrete sleepers; simple elastic spikes driven into wood/fibre inserts.

The only type of timber still in regular use for sleepers are the hardwoods, jarrah, karri and similar woods, imported from Australia and other sources. The wood is excellent for crossing timbers. It is not a new idea. In 1902 jarrah was used on the GWR Badminton line and the sleepers lasted 22 years to 30 years but despite this long life the experiment was not considered a complete success as the wood did not grip onto the ballast and the track tended to go out of alignment and 'creep'.

More information on long welded rails, switches and crossings, and fastenings is given in following Chapters but it is hoped the reader will now appreciate the background history to the permanent way on which the safe passage of his train depends.

Chapter Four

Redbridge Works and its Products

When the Works closed early in 1989 it had a number of departments, all with modern machinery and equipment. They were:-

1. Foundry, pattern shop and stores to produce iron castings.
2. Flash-butt welding plant with associated lifting and rail conveying equipment to produce long welded running rail or electric conductor rail.
3. Machine shop to produce track components for switches and crossings etc.
4. Pre-assembly yard for laying out complex track produced at the Works prior to moving the 'broken-down' sections by train to the site of track-laying.
5. Sawmill for cutting bridge timbers and other sections from baulks.
6. Recovery area for dismantling redundant chaired track for scrap.

These departments had organisational, management, clerical and stores back-up and services such as fire fighting, heating, water and power supplies. It is interesting to notice that the original reason for Redbridge Works, the handling and storage of timber sleepers, had been eclipsed by the task of producing modern track components. The story must, however start with timber sleepers, standard, for ordinary track, 10in wide, 5in thick and 9ft long.

The choice of Redbridge as a depot was made because it had a wharf, a useful, large area of open land for storage, tidal mudflats for seasoning ponds and rail facilities to all parts of the system. From 1880 and for the ensuing 90 years, sleepers were its primary concern.

In the late 19th century and for the first half of the 20th the normal practice of the London & South Western Railway, its successor, the Southern Railway and other principal railways in Britain was to import pine, fir or redwood sawn sleepers cut to size as at the sawmills in the country of origin. The timber was softwood and the Baltic countries, and in more recent years Canada, were the usual sources. Many Baltic ports including those on the north European coast, Dantzig and Riga, were used as points of loading. Hardwood sleepers were too expensive for general use and had other disadvantages although they had a much greater resistance to rot and decay. Some were introduced on the early electrified lines in London, partly because of their fire resisting qualities, but later uses of jarrah and similar woods on

Sleepers being unloaded from the *S.S. Northgate* and from barges about 1926. Four steam cranes are busy and the sleepers are stacked fifty-two high. Men would climb to the tops of these stacks using the protruding ends as steps!
British Rail

The *S.S. Battersonian* berthing at the wharf in June 1924, with a cargo of new SI chairs from Middlesbrough. It returned with a similar cargo of second-hand chairs to Messrs Smith Patterson. The vessel carried a brass plate on the bridge recording that it had rammed and sunk a German submarine in the First World War.

Sleeper barges being unloaded at the Wharf in January, 1924. This crane, many years later, was turned over onto the edge of the timber pond. The driver, George Oak, fortunately jumped clear.

View looking from the south-east of the site across the timber pond and the Wharf in June 1924. The chimney above the sleeper stacks is on the former linseed oil mill building. *All photos, British Rail*

the L&SWR and SR were normally confined to crossing timbers or special locations. Oak and hemlock were also used when redwoods were in short supply. Other heavy section softwood timber, for example for baulk timbers for bridges, was usually imported as logs, unsawn and these were seasoned and dried before being cut to size in the Works saw mill.

Deliveries of sleepers were made to Redbridge wharf in small sea-going vessels or by barges loaded from larger boats which had discharged their cargoes at Southampton. Sailing ships had been largely displaced by steam at about the time Redbridge was opened. The wharf was also used for landing other materials, rail, chairs and fishplates. Perhaps it was inevitable that there were a number of incidents in the early days!

For example, on 6th August, 1884 the steamship 'Dollie' was discharging rails when James Gray, a ships' fireman, fell overboard into the river and was drowned. At the inquest the railway company were criticized for the lack of means for saving anyone accidentally falling into the water and they were recommended to provide four lifebuoys and lines, two moveable ladders with chains and a stretcher in addition to the buoys and grapnels already there. In the previous year there had been two fatalities, one human and one a horse used for hauling timbers. No doubt lessons were learnt.

Deliveries of raw sleepers to Redbridge tended to be seasonal, with a big rush in the spring and early summer, because the Baltic Sea was frozen in the winter. Similarly the St. Lawrence in Canada was impassable for shipping in the winter months. Trees were preferably felled in the autumn and left to season before the timber was cut into sleepers at the sawmills shortly before shipment to this country. On arrival at Redbridge the sleepers had to be carefully unloaded and stacked. Any unnecessary damage was avoided and men were given strict instructions on the way they handled sleepers so that the ingress of decay was minimised

The first job after unloading was to stack the sleepers so that they could be thoroughly dried out. Stacks of about 160 sleepers were built on a prepared dry area, eight sleepers each way with air spaces about 4in, laid criss-cross pattern, 20 or more high, so that air, light and warmth could freely circulate in the stack. The two top layers were laid with the sleepers only 1in apart and the stack was 'roofed' with more sleepers laid at an angle. The illustration shows that some stacked sleepers in the early 1920's were also bored for chair screws before stacking. Stacks could be much higher than those shown; some were 'towers', blocks over 50 high. Sleepers remained drying in these stacks for seasoning for between six and twelve months.

Decay has already been mentioned and most railways adopted the well known preservative, creosote, to treat sleepers before use. Creosote is a product from coal tar and was obtained from local gasworks through the distillery at Eling. At Redbridge open tanks or vats were built in 1881/2 into which bundles of sleepers were placed and 'soaked' for weeks or even months. The operation of 'chairing' the sleepers was carried out alongside the tanks. In July, 1883 approval was given to roofing over the area of the tanks and the space used for chairing sleepers. No doubt this improved working conditions.

Prior to creosoting, the required number of holes near each end were bored for the chair fastenings and the surface of the sleeper was adzed to prepare it to carry the bases of the chairs. These operations were soon carried out automatically by ingenious adzing and boring machines designed to handle and convey sleepers with a minimum of labour. The usual layout on a machine was for the sleepers to be fed crosswise onto the auguring bed where the holes were bored, and this operation was followed by the adzing cutters to surface the areas on which the chairs were

Right: The newly arrived sleepers are stacked for seasoning. View looking south across the river to Marchwood.

Below: Portable elevators, called 'Camels' were used to help the men making stacks. On the left of the crane is a pile of logs for seasoning in the pond behind.

Both, British Rail

to seat. The adzing/boring machine installed in 1937 also had two circular saws to cut the sleeper to length.

Pressure creosoting of timber was invented about 1838, the Bethell or Full Cell Process being the oldest and it was this technique that was adopted by most railway companies for sleeper preservation. Different railways used different pressure conditions and times but basically the principles were the same. The plant was comprised one or more, above-ground, long cylindrical steel pressure vessels, typically 80ft long and 7ft diameter with hinged hemispherical doors at both ends. Loads of untreated sleepers on narrow gauge rail trolleys were run into the cylinders, the doors were closed tightly, air was exhausted and after up to an hour, the tanks were filled with hot creosote and then pressurised to about 100 to 150 lbs/sq. in. After treatment the creosote was allowed to drain off and sometimes this was assisted by another vacuum run. The trolleys of treated sleepers were then removed for chairing. Some companies re-stacked sleepers for at least six

weeks before use so that the creosote hardened and the sleeper dried.

Pressure creosoting was introduced and an adzing and boring machine installed at Redbridge Works, in the plant built in 1922/23. There were two creosoting tanks, each 75ft long and 7ft diameter. These were located above three concrete underground storage tanks with a total capacity of over 90,000 gallons of creosote. In the floor of the storage tanks were steam heated pipes to raise the temperatures of the liquid to 130'F. Old locomotive type boilers were used to raise steam until they were replaced in 1965 by new oil fired boilers. One charge in one pressure cylinder took 464 sleepers on narrow gauge rail trolleys. The vacuum/pressure/vacuum cycle described above was used but the pressure, 200 lbs/sq.in was higher than some pre-1914 plants. Electrically driven vacuum and pressure pumps were employed and an absorption of 10lbs of creosote per cu.ft. could be achieved on suitable timber.

Unloading the treated sleepers from the trolleys hauled out of the cylinders is remembered by former Redbridge employees as a shocking job! The fumes of the creosote, the oily nature of the timber and the way the smell would penetrate clothing, the hair and the skin can well be imagined. The manual handling involved lifting the heavy impregnated sleepers onto the table of the chairing machines which were purpose built to place and fasten chairs, each weighing about 46lb, onto the timber with screws or bolts. They were then automatically elevated by the machine to open rail wagons where other men stacked them for dispatch to a site or to the yard for storage.

The Canadian Douglas fir sleepers imported from about 1940, (due to wartime closing of European sources of timber), were difficult to treat. This type of fir absorbs only small amounts of preservative and penetration is poor and the problem led to the introduction in 1964, at a cost of £4600, of an incising machine used prior to treatment. The fir sleepers were passed through a machine provided with spring-loaded rollers each equipped with thin removable cutting knives designed to part the fibres of the wood without crushing or breaking them. Incising gave much

21

Above: In 1922 the London and South Western Railway decided to further develop Redbridge Works. This view, taken on 31st October 1923, looking north-east across the yard, shows the extensive new works underway. The steelwork of the stores building has been erected. Beyond are the station platforms and in the centre is the rail weightbridge which still stood in 1989. The shed and foundations for the creosoting plant are being erected.

Left: By January 1924 the pressure creosoting tanks were in position. This view is looking west towards the station, along sidings parallel with the main line.   *Both, British Rail*

Loaded bogies with raw sleepers being pushed into pressure creosoting cylinders. A system of capstan haulage with wire ropes was used to draw the impregnated sleepers out of the cylinders.   *British Rail*

improved creosote 'take-up' and the marks or indents on a sleeper may be seen on the picture. The incising machine was sold in a 1976 to a firm at Freemantle, Australia for £6000. The same firm bought the 1937 adzer-borer for £2000.

In the days before concrete sleepers, Redbridge handled, in the spring and summer months, between ¾ million and a million timber sleepers and stored, typically, between 250,000 and 300,000 sleepers in the yard. The capacity for producing chaired and treated sleepers was 1700 a day. On 19th June, 1940 the first German air raid took place on Southern Railway property and Redbridge was hit. One high explosive bomb destroyed 7000 sleepers and 2000 pieces of crossing timber while another damaged the wharf front and buildings housing the adzing and boring machinery. The engineer's staff localised the conflagration but the policy of dispersal of the stock of sleepers who quickly accelerated. Before the raid 20,000 had already gone to various points on the system but after the event one or two trains a day were run to twenty locations for a three weeks period. Assistance in loading was given by 50 Royal Engineer Sappers. The less inflammable jarrah sleepers were kept at the depot and alternate hardwood and softwood stacks were formed to reduce the risk of the spread of fire.

For over 70 years cargoes of sleepers were unloaded at the wharf on Redbridge Channel by ships derricks or cranes using chain or rope slings. Once landed the problem was to move the timbers to stacks. Originally wagons were hauled by horses but steam rail cranes were soon introduced and rail tracks were laid to give circular loops with reasonable access to the storage areas.

In 1922/23 a ferro-concrete gantry for a travelling crane was built from the wharf at right angles to the quay and this increased the speed of unloading and achieved rapid unloading of rail wagons. Wagons could then be moved using the steam cranes for shunting and offloading. Additionally, a large radius 5 ton derrick crane was built which had a reach of about 60ft.

In World War Two women employees were engaged on this heavy work; photograph taken on 22nd February 1943.   *British Rail*

Stacks were originally formed by manual labour but portable conveyors or 'Camels' were introduced as shown in the picture on page   . Despite all this handling machinery the work was arduous and the men employed became very skilled at climbing stacks, throwing down sleepers into wagons and carrying out their duties without serious injury. It was a 'way of life' on the often bleak and windswept wharf and yards of Redbridge. But it was an era that ended with the introduction of concrete sleepers. By 1964 the timber sleeper for new main line plain track was superceded by the BR standard reinforced concrete sleeper.'

As a result of this revolutionary change in the traditional material the wharf at Redbridge fell into disuse, the creosoting plant was closed and the areas for stacking became empty. The last full time use of the machinery was in 1969 but there was some part time use up to 1974, producing sleepers for the LMR at Ditton. The vessels, tanks, pumps and storage were demolished in 1978.

Before considering other track components made at Redbridge the background to the introduction of ferro-concrete sleepers as standard for welded-rail track should be mentioned. Although there were experiments with the material in the 1900's it gained little favour until the second war when timber and steel were both in short supply. For sidings, goods loops and on a few lightly operated branch lines, independent block sleepers with every third or fourth pair connected by steel ties were used. Heavy traverse concrete sleepers were also introduced to replace timber and these were reinforced with simple steel wire-mesh.

In post war years the design was developed for flat-bottom as well as bull head and numerous types were track tested by the main line companies. Problems of fastening the rail to the sleeper exercised the ingenuity of designers and many types of clip, spike and patent fastening may still be seen (see illustrations). Also, the importance of maintaining the resilience offered by timber had to be pursued. Passengers will recognise the need of a 'soft' ride and may recall riding on track which gave a feeling of being on a 'hard' and unyielding track. To improve the 'ride' and the inherent damage to rolling stock by non-resilient track, pads of felt, rubber or plastic were introduced between the rail and the concrete sleeper or between the rail and a bedplate on the sleeper.

Pre-stressed concrete sleepers, (about four times heavier than a softwood timber sleeper), are now the standard for the main lines of British Railways. The reinforcement is by pre-tensioned wires or tendons along the length of the sleeper and the malleable iron fixings for the rail fastening clips are cast into the concrete at the manufacturers works. As from 1966 the 'Pandrol Clip' has been the standard fastening and the rail rests on a resilient pad of rubber-bonded cork or rubber laid on the sleeper. There may also be a small nylon insulator placed between the Pandrol clip and the rail to provide electrical insulation.

The illustrations show a number of developments in flat bottom track which has displaced traditional chaired bull head on creosoted wood sleepers in the past 20 years. However, there is still plenty of old type track to see and it is an interesting exercise to spy the differences on your travels.

Above: A stack of standard F24 prestressed concrete sleepers. Rails are held on each side at every sleeper by Pandrol spring clips which are driven into the eyes cast into the sleepers at manufacture. The cut ends of the reinforcing wire tendons can be seen at the sleeper ends.

Left: These new sleepers are for third-rail electrified track. The four holes at one end of each sleeper take the bolts to secure the insulators. The 20° angled bed for the rail can be seen on this end view of stacked sleepers.

Both, John Fairman

Until 1950 the foundry was situated at the west end of the yard, latterly the building became the machine shop. This picture, taken on 3rd December 1945 from the vantage point of the gantry crane walkway, shows the two cupolas, (above the crane), a yard congested with internal use wagons, and stock piles of chairs and rail. Bryce White's timber sheds, on the north side of the railway, are beyond the cupolas. *British Rail*

The Foundry

Railway track needs a whole range of iron castings. The most obvious is the ordinary chair, that heavy jawed baseplate to carry the bull-head rail on a sleeper. More complex check-chair castings are required where there are double or check rails on curves and there are many variations of rail support and spacing on any set of points or crossings. Terms like end-chairs, knuckle-chairs and wing-chairs are well known to the track engineer. Flat bottom rail needs sole plates and these too are complex on switches and crossings.

In 1924/5 the newly-formed Southern Railway decided to pursue their policy of self sufficiency by the manufacture at Red-bridge, of iron castings and in particular switch and crossing rail chairs. Prior to that time the L&SWR's normal practice had been to buy finished castings from outside foundries, although some materials, especially special components, had been cast at the locomotive works at Nine Elms and later at Eastleigh. It is an interesting exercise to examine chairs and to identify the foundry by its initials, the date of casting, and the type.

The first small foundry and pattern shop at Redbridge in 1924 was near the west end of the site and it occupied the section that later became the machine shop and a mess room. The production was set at a maximum of 48 tons a week. Within a few years this was inadequate and the dirt and noise associated with the foundry near the site entrance and the offices made a move essential. In 1926 the Schultz Gunpowder factory land at the far eastern end of the Works was acquired by the Southern Railway and most of the buildings demolished. The foundry moved to this site in 1933. The new foundry had a capacity of up to 58 tons a week from two cupolas or melting furnaces.

Plans were made in 1936 to improve the capacity to 80 tons of castings a week by investment of £7800 in better plant, thereby reducing costs from £2. 3. 6d to £1. 6. 6d a ton. Unfortunately, the war intervened and the project had to be shelved until 1946. By that time the cost of castings had risen to £14 7.7d a ton; and an estimated investment of £38,400 was required to produce 80 tons a week at £12. 8.4d a ton.

This scheme was eventually implemented and a new foundry was built in 1950 adjacent to the 1933 premises. Some of the old buildings became 'support units' for the new; for example, for the pattern store, core making and core cleaning. Mr R.G. Baker, for so many years the Works manager first came to Redbridge as the resident engineer during the 1950

Looking north-east at the new foundry building, on 27th July 1951. The two 3-ton cupolas can be seen. On the left are three bays of the powder factory, retained as the pattern shop and stores.

Internal view of the layout of the 1951 foundry showing, left, sand plant conveyor and hoppers, also the overhead runways for carrying ladles of molten metal from cupolas to moulding boxes, and the roller tracks for boxes. Some floor moulding was continued where boxes were large. The plant was very dirty despite a dust extraction plant. *Both, British Rail*

Right: The passing of a Redbridge landmark. On 14th July 1927 the old Schultz powder factory chimney, at the east end of the site, was felled to clear the land for re-development for the new foundry.

Below: An official visit on 7th August 1974 by the General Manager, (now BR Chairman), Sir Robert Reid. Les Blackmore, furnaceman, taps the cupola watched by, left to right, Geoffrey Cope, Permanent Way Engineer; Mr Reid; Mike Bidwell, Production Manager; and Len Harvey, Administrative Assistant.   *Both, British Rail*

The stock yard for foundry products and for 'bought-in' components was east of the foundry on a part of the old Schultz factory land. This view, looking west, is from the foundry and pattern shop. A siding ran along the north, (right), side parallel with the main line to receive and load material. In the foreground are crossing chairs for 95lb bull head rail, cast in August 1988. *John Fairman*

Sanding a moulding box. Ivan Smith, Works Manager until his sad death in December 1987, points out to Sir Robert the job being carried out by the moulder, Dave Reed. *British Rail*

Pouring molten iron from the ladle into moulding boxes. Tony Barton and Fred Cox are the foundrymen. *British Rail*

A close-up view of the new cupolas, as fitted in 1951. *Jim Hodgson Collection*

Above: The Pattern Shop in 1951 with Chief Patternmaker Bishop at the bandsaw. He lived in 'The Bungalow'. *Jim Hodgson Collection*

Left: A skilled pattern-maker, Arthur Willis. Patterns were usually made of mahogany and were replicas of the iron article to be cast. The pattern shop at Redbridge included a full range of woodworking machinery and benches for six patternmakers. *British Rail*

reconstruction. Despite being the third 'new' plant the concept was obsolete. Only floor casting was used, that is, with the moulds on the floor, and hand ladles were used to pour the molten iron tapped from the cupolas. The cupolas each had a capacity of 3 tons an hour. Moulding sand was brought to the moulds by an old fashioned overhead push-plate conveyor. The noise and dirt is remembered 40 years later! Output did not come up to expectations and high costs and poor productivity from the labour intensive plant were revealed by 1964 figures of £41 a ton and a weekly output of only 26 tons.

In 1967/8 the eight to ten hand-moulding positions were replaced by some mechanisation; two sets of pneumatically-operated moulding machines made by BMM Weston Ltd were introduced to replace all but two of the hand positions, also twin roller lines to facilitate the handling of moulding boxes. The duty of the moulding machines was to ensure a vigorous compaction of the sand around all the interstices of the mould and thereby

29

The back of the foundry, 3rd August 1988. The taller cupolas were built in 1971. The 'Medfit' wagons for scrap iron (see Appendix) replaced five-plank wagons.   *John Fairman*

to assist in the production of good quality castings. This plant cost £20,000 and pushed weekly output up to 70 tons, still at £40 a ton. However, the situation continued to deteriorate and by 1977 costs had soared to £140 a ton and production had fallen to 50 tons a week. Drastic action, or closure, was needed.

Happily an investment in a modern sand plant was approved and installed in 1977 at a cost of £200,000. This comprised pneumatic conveyors to replace the old mechanical conveyors and it increased the potential output to 90 tons a week although the level of production was rarely needed. Early in 1988 a further major improvement was made; a continuous conveyor was installed to carry the boxes while the castings cooled on their journey round the building. An output of 50 to 60 castings a day was the practical production level at the end of the foundry's life, plus the output from three or four hand moulders. Raw materials for the cupolas was scrap castings, (reclaimed chairs, etc.), coke and limestone. Latterly the coke was delivered by 20 tonnes lorries direct from France; formerly it came from British coke ovens. In 1971 the cupolas were replaced by the final two units, taller than their predecessors, and 30in internal diameter. Their capacity was 5 tons of iron an hour. Each cupola was used on alternative days to allow maintenance to be carried out, usually fireclay spraying. Cupolas were started up overnight by lighting up a 12 cwt charge with a gas torch and then, in the morning, bringing up to heat with the fan.

There were two main production lines and standard greensand moulding was used. Patterns, and there were over 6000 then in the pattern store, were of mahogany or less usually of aluminium or plastic. Some Great Western Railway patterns were of iron. The ladles of molten iron tapped from the cupolas were moved to pouring points along overhead runway tracks and the layout was well designed. Of interest is the fact that there was a loss of about 15% sand during casting. Tests were carried out three times a day to check the sand being recycled for its permeability and moisture content, ideally 3%. A proprietory mixture of bentonite/coal dust and starch was added to maintain quality.

The foundry was re-roofed in 1987 and a new Omega sand-reclamation unit delivered in 1988. This unit was to have been used in connection with a different moulding process, using silica sand and a resin for box moulding. By the addition of carbon dioxide gas the mould produced was stable for weeks whereas a greensand mould was no use after 12 to 24 hours. The reclamation unit was necessary because it would have been too expensive to waste the silica. Alas, it was too late to be installed before the foundry closed. The final castings were poured in the foundry on 6th October, 1988.

Pictorial view looking west on 27th July 1951, showing the first plant. In the building was the flash butt welder and the post-heating plant. Hand-operated pneumatic chipping hammers were used to remove the set metal after welding and hand grinders were used to finish off the weld after post-heating. An overhead gantry and a 2-ton Vaughan crane was provided in the assembly area. Eling Wharf is across the river.   *British Rail*

The Production of the Long Welded Rail

Once Bessemer steel rails had displaced wrought iron it was the ability of the rolling mills that dictated the maximum length of a rail. Handling and transport problems were also considerations and a standard length of 45ft was common for new deliveries to the L&SWR by the 1880's. Later, 60ft rail was more usual.

The weakest point in all jointed rail track is at the butt ends of consecutive rails and the fishplated link or strap between the rails has always been the subject of intensive study. Fishplates were invented by W.B. Adams and R. Richardson in 1847 and were soon adopted for British double head and bull head rails. The fishplate helped support the ends of the rails as well as keeping them in line. Hence the familiar four-bolt fishplate which gave good support and thereby reduced the wear on rails at the butt joints.

Everyone knows the need to allow for the expansion and contraction of rails with variations in temperature. Elongated pear-shaped holes in fishplates for the bolts permitted the expansion. We all remember the creaking noise as rails expanded when the sun came out on a hot summer day! The bar type steel fishplate was designed to grip the upper and lower heads of the rail and not to touch the web so that, when the $\frac{7}{8}$in or 1in dia. bolts were tightened the ends of the rail were firmly held. Fishplates are always greased to allow movement and to keep bolts from seizing.

Clearly, to reduce the damage and failure of rail ends and to give a quieter and smoother ride, a reduction in the number of rail joints was a most desirable objective but no progress could be made until the technique of rail welding had been developed. In 1899 and 1900 a German engineer, Professor Goldschmidt, experimented with his 'Thermit' method of welding for tramway rails in Essen. This method uses the very exothermic reaction between Ferric Oxide and Aluminium to fuse the steel, both powders being contained in a refractory mould formed around the ends of the rails to be welded. In 1929, the Southern Railway made a test of the Thermit system on bull head track when, in conjunction with Murex Ltd, rails were welded together at Worplesdon. This was a 'one-off' experiment and it was London Transport who, in 1937, carried out the pioneering work in Britain and made up 300ft lengths of rail welded by the Thermit process.

Overseas, notably on the Continent, in America and Australia, good progress had been made towards the entire elimination of joints over long lengths of track by the adoption of electric flash-butt depot welding techniques. Again, the Germans were first in the field and made long rail lengths by this process in 1928. In 1933 representatives of the LNER and Southern Railways visited Berlin to witness the operation. In 1935, London Transport, (LPTB), set up the first UK long

Above: The long flash butt-welded rails continued along a roller track to the overhead gantry, built in 1950, where they were handled across to rail wagons at a loading platform. This was at the far eastern end of the site.

Left: The 1949 A1 welder in spectacular action. In the early days, the work carried out was often to make long lengths from many short pieces.

Both, British Rail

Right: The 1949 post-heating plant, left, and the welder at the far end. Rails on the roller track were hand-propelled and completed LWR was pushed out to the dispatch loading dock.

Below: 2nd November 1949. The welding shop and the table with short lengths of rail for loading onto the roller track for welding.

Both, British Rail

welded rail production line. It was at their Lillie Bridge depot and their work on Thermit welded rails is referred to above. LT continued to produce LWR for their system and had more in use than all the rest of the railways in Britain put together. The first A1 flash-butt welder made by the Inverness company was installed at Lillie Bridge in 1946 and all long welded rails for other railways in the UK were made there, prior to 1947.

Flash-butt welding consists essentially of bringing into contact the two pieces of metal to be welded, and passing a heavy current at low voltage through them. The resistance at the faces of contact causes an increase in heat to forging temperature. The two faces are then forced together under pressure and a weld is formed. In the LWR plant installed at Redbridge in 1949 the FB welding unit was the standard type made by A1 Welding Ltd. Rails were correctly positioned in the welding unit, ends butting, horizontally and vertically aligned, and then clamped between heavy jaw blocks of copper alloy. One pair of jaw blocks remained

stationary and the other was free to be moved by the welding machine, backwards and forwards, a small distance, longitudinally with the rail it was holding. Actual welding was carried out in three stages; preheating, flashing and 'upsetting'.

Preheating to the required welding temperature was obtained by passing a heavy amperage, low voltage, electric current through the rails and at the same time bringing the moveable rail into contact and then moving it away again, repeating the movement cycle until the correct temperature was reached. When the flashing stage was carried out the rails were pressed together at a predetermined rate while a continuous flow of current was passed through the rails. For the 'upsetting' stage the current was switched off and the rail was 'rammed' home against the fixed end with a pressure of about 20 tons. This final thrust made an effective weld and surplus metal was extruded round the periphery of the rails at the point of the fusion. The subsequent stages of the work were carried out in a post heating furnace and in a profile grinding machine.

The first Redbridge FB welding plant was commissioned in 1950. It was similar to the plant built at Chesterton for the Eastern Region and was located at the east end of the Works, parallel with the shore. It cost over £100,000 but its lifting gantries were only capable of handling 180ft lengths and this limited its capability. It was first used for making long-welded lengths for installation on bridges and for welding up shorts to make standard length rails. Then it was used for welding lengths of conductor rails for the post-war electrification projects in Kent but by 1962 the plant was in use for welding running rails. Welds were ground smooth by handheld portable grinders and the operators had to stand in a pit to be at the right level for using their machines. Forward movement of the lengths was by rope and winch haulage and the plant was a quaint mix of 'ancient and modern'. A one-ton 'Tup' dead-weight drop tester was used to determine the weld quality on which the weight was dropped from a predetermined height onto the sample rail being checked. Latterly a hydraulic ram tester was used to establish deflection figures on load.

The rail conveyor between the rail-end cleaning plant and the welding plant. Behind are the overhead cranes and the feed-table.

Self-propelled trains to take LWR to relaying sites were introduced in 1987, although they were locomotive hauled to or from Redbridge Works. George Elmes, maintenance foreman, stands in front of Unit No. 11 on 3rd August 1988. *Both, John Fairman*

A close-up of the angled feed-table for lengths of rail for the flash butt welding plant. Note the electric motor driven rollers.

The rail stacking area under the Demag travelling crane electro-magnets. The shunting locomotive is Class 09, 09026.

Above: The first flash butt welder was replaced in 1962 and the installation was transformed and fully mechanised. The building was extended and this view in August 1988 shows the welding plant, right, and post-weld treatment units further along the electrically powered rail roller-conveyor.

Right: The assembly area after reconstruction. The building housed the rail end-cleaning plant. Behind it there was the roller-conveyor feed table with angled power rollers. New rails for welding were offloaded from wagons by two gantry cranes spanning the yard. They were new in 1982 and replaced the Vaughan crane. Lifting was by magnet or hook and the cranes were used to place rail lengths for welding onto the feed table.

All photos, John Fairman

The dispatch area looking east in August 1988. Long welded 113 lb/yard FB rails are identified by numbers. The dispatch platform is on the left and the roller conveyor on the right.
John Fairman

The development of the use of long welded rail had to be paralleled by quite revolutionary progress in the designs of track in post war years. To contain the stresses within the rails caused by atmospheric temperature fluctuations, the whole track had to be of a higher standard, well aligned, to have strong sleepers with required stability on good deep ballast, and to have robust rail fastenings. These elements were introduced in the 1950's and 1960's. The standard 109 and 113 lb/yard flat bottom rail, heavy pre-stressed concrete and jarrah sleepers, Pandrol and other designs of clips, resilient pads, uniform beds of deep ballast below the sleepers and advanced relaying techniques are all products of the quest for a smoother ride and lower maintenance costs for track associated with the long welded rail.

In 1962/3 the first Redbridge flash-butt welding plant was replaced and the whole installation was completely reconstructed. A new A1 welder incorporating a weld stripper was installed, a rail assembly line was built at the west end of the plant, and the loading gantries for the LWR at the east end were extended and modernised to handle 600ft lengths. In 1982 the assembly and stocking area further developed by the installation of two fine Demag electric overhead travelling cranes spanning 110ft across the stocking area for new rails and across three rail sidings. A angled powered loading roller deck covering a length of 150ft were introduced and this automated the feed of rail lengths onto a motorised rail conveyor supplied by GEC Ltd. The single-line conveyor was 1650ft long, extending from the loading deck, through a small building with a wet shot blasting rail-end cleaner, then through the long single-storey brick LWR shed which housed the welding plant, a spray cooler, power press and profile and alignment checker, and a grinder. Only three men were required to operate the whole plant. The cooler, press and grinder were made by a Swiss firm, Nencki Hydraulok, under the name Matix Saferail. Finally the conveyor took the LWR lengths out into the yard ready for dispatch to relaying sites.

Each Demag crane had a SWL, (safe working load), of 6.15 tonnes with magnet or 10 tons with non-magnet use and was capable of lifting rail from the stockyard or from rail wagons using twin magnets carried on a beam. Six 60ft rails was the normal load for one crane. Two cranes were used for six 120ft lengths. The crane track ran parallel with the LWR production line conveyor and extended to 400ft, the whole length of the stockyard and very impressive they looked in their bright yellow livery.

The arrangements in the dispatch yard were originally very basic! When a full length of LWR was ready for loading sideways onto rail wagons berthed alongside the loading bank, 14 men were required, one for each hand-operated chain lifting block to lift each rail. When all the hooks had been attached they raised the load evenly, then, to get the rail onto the wagon, they climbed onto the rail and set up a swinging action. Thus, in unison they swung it across, leaping off as it landed! The facilities in the latterday plant used the same reinforced concrete columns and steel cross-beams but handling was controlled from a central point. The 14 hoists had been replaced by 2 ton electric units, each with its pendant control. Once each hoist had been dogged onto the rail to be lifted and slack had been taken up, all hoisting and traversing across to the rail wagons was controlled from a cabin halfway along the area.

The land at the far eastern end of Redbridge Works was once used for farming and rough grazing. The last tenant, Andrew Southwell vacated the site in the 1960's and it became very overgrown. Latterly it was quite a nature reserve with a fascinating collection of flowers and wildlife. Foxes were frequently seen, sea birds of many species could be identified on the estuary mudflats and there was one location where a bed of rushes marked the last visible section of the Salisbury Canal.

In the 1950's the quality of welds from the flash-butt welder was tested by taking random samples and subjecting the test pieces to the impact of a weight dropped from a height. This was called a 'Tup' test. The rig is shown to the right. Above are the results of two tests, one obviously unsuccessful.

Immediately after welding, and before post heating, welds were fettled by hand, using a pneumatic chisel. Here, on 2nd November 1949, Stan Brixton demonstrates the operation watched by Jim Hodgson and other colleagues. Modern engineers will deplore the lack of safety goggles.

All photos British Rail

Machine Shops

The switches and crossings on our railways are fascinating assemblies of specially manufactured components and for over 60 years Redbridge played a very important role in their production. As recently as 1988 they were making and assembling materials for a revised layout at Bishops Stortford, Essex, in connection with the new branch to Stanstead Airport and crossings for Stage 1 of the remodelling at Clapham Jc. was the last major job carried out in the machine shops.

Look carefully at the form of switch design at your local station. There are straight track switches with curved crossings or with straight crossings, double curved or 'contra flexure' switches, crossover roads, diamond and scissors crossings. The variation are almost endless. On a switch, the tongue rails or point 'blades' rest against the stock, or outside, rails. The tongue rails are connected by stretcher bars. Consider the problem of machining, (planing), the tongue rails from full section new rail, especially on a long switch. Much of the machinery for rail planing was specially designed and the work was often carried out by specialist firms. Similarly, the design of crossings, where rails allow the flanged wheel to cross another rail, are most ingenious.

Consider the task of bending rail to form the wing rail or rails forming the outside rails of a crossing, or machining and maybe welding the point rail and the splice rail where they come together to a nose at the X of the crossing, and the work involved in making check rails forming the inside rails opposite a crossing. All have special chairs or bedplates, bolts, spacer blocks and all the components have to be manufactured and assembled. Many railway companies used specialist firms on this work and for the last 30 or more years it has been British Rail policy to let the work to private industry. Redbridge was therefore, fortunate in retaining its extensive production facilities right up to 1989 and was the last BR Works capable of the manufacturing the full range of track components and assemblies.

It is possible that some old fashioned belt-driven machinery may have existed at Redbridge Works before the Southern Railway was formed in 1923. If so, these early machine tools would have been in the building originally used as the oil and cake mills of Dixon & Cardus, opposite the site entrance. No details are recorded.

The machine tools for manufacturing components for switches and crossings were usually purpose-made. This 20ft planer was supplied by John Stirk & Sons, Halifax, in 1924 and had a moving bed. Lengths of bull-head rail for machining are in the foreground. *British Rail*

An additional machine shop was built in 1970/1. This photograph was taken on 24th November 1970. Local people will notice the change in the skyline.
British Rail

The 30ft and 40ft bed Stirk planers were four-tool machines and they were fine examples of the modern equipment in the new shop at Redbridge.
British Rail

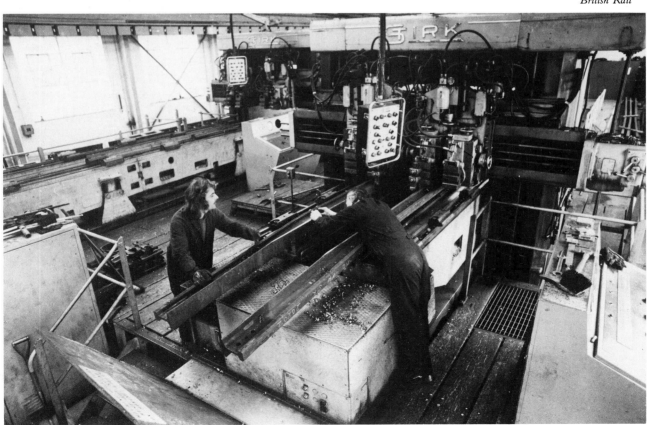

Switches, points and crossings are, of course, made from steel rail and the very special production requires suitable presses, planing, milling, shaping, cutting, drilling and other machinery, some being of purpose built design. In 1924 the first tools were obtained to equip a new machine shop at Redbridge. They were:-

A 12ft switch planer
An 8ft V-planer
A 20ft Stirk planer
A Leeds hydraulic press (worked from a hydraulic accumulator)

All these machines had a long working life and they were joined in 1933 by a specialist 'point and splice' planer which was brought into use in the workshop vacated by the foundry. Other good quality second-hand machines were added; from Brighton Works when it closed in 1962, came a 1941 Laudon planer which was useful for machining wing and check rails and from Swindon Works in 1966 a 35ft-stroke planer was acquired for use in making the longer blades of high-speed turn-outs. It cannot be overstressed that machining, drilling and other work on the manufacture of switches and crossings had to be of a very high level of accuracy. Although rail is 'heavy metal' the skill and precision required of the machinists was of the highest calibre and their workmanship was always of admirable quality.

Up to 1971 the machine tools at Redbridge were only suitable for British Standard carbon steel rail but the increasing use of manganese alloy steels for the construction of switches and crossings in intensively used locations brought a need to be able to machine these harder steels. The first manganese steel crossings had been installed on the Central London Railway in 1902 and

Above: Machining a Vee for a crossing. Joe Mole is the machininst.
British Rail
Left: A fabricated manganese steel crossing showing a welded and machined Vee. *John Fairman*

Below: Cast manganese steel crossings. The raised check rail on this design has caused problems with long wheelbase steam locomotives.
John Fairman

their resistance to abrasive wear was proved to be quite superb. Messrs. Hadfields, Edgar Allens and a French manufacturer became the principal suppliers of cast manganese crossings and manganese steel rails but in the 1970's the high cost was only considered justified for complex layouts, for example on the well known crossings outside Newcastle or on busy electrified lines. For the Southern Region, a completely new machine shop was built in 1971 at Redbridge to house the latest 30ft and 40ft planers, with an electro-hydraulic bending press, an abrasive saw and an Asquith drill which was able to drill through manganese steel rail. The cost of the whole installation was £250,000.

The original machine shop continued in use for some time and was supplied with three additional machines; two further drills, and a Horbrough shaper to make 'let-ins' for point and splice rails. One small new building was also added which was a separate room for tool and drill sharpening. Until the Works closed the 'former foundry' machine shop at the west end of the yard opposite the site of the locomotive shed was still in active use. Rail for machining was fed into the shop from the west end on roller tracks. Inside, there was a 2 ton Allen overhead travelling crane. The principal machines were two 30ft Butler planers with moving beds and an Asquith 30ft planer with a fixed bed and a moving consul. There were also grinders, an Invicta and Milwaukee shaper, and a saw. The next section was served by a 1½ ton crane and included a Cincinatti miller and a Finlay electro-hydraulic press for forming wing and check rails and for general rail bending work.

Between this machine shop and the quay was a low brick building accommodating the welding shop, the blacksmith's shop, (closed in 1986), and the shop for the maintenance department.

By 1978 further investment in the machine shops was required and a fine new workshop extension was built to the east of the 'foundry' shop. Many of the machines in the old shop dated from 1924 and were worn out and were replaced. In the post-war years there had been many developments in milling and, cutting and other techniques for machining steel. British Rail Board had also made further progress on the use introduction of manganese steel switches and swtich diamonds and this material required additional welding plant and justified improvements in the whole technique of rail handling and welding. Two fine new four-tool Stirk planers, one with a 30ft and one with a 40ft machining capability were installed in 1979, also new drilling machines and the facilities to weld hard alloy-steel point and splice rails, and to machine manganese forgings. The new workshop was equipped with a 3 ton Street overhead travelling crane and also housed a Clifford & Baird circular saw, the Spenstead disc cutter, a press and other modern machine tools. At its east end a switch assembly bay was built, served by a 6 ton Street overhead crane and provided with a rail siding for loading wagons with completed work. All this machinery and these workshop facilities remained in use to the end of production in 1989.

It is hoped to convey to the 'lay' reader by the illustrations the size and complexity of some of the modern machines in use at the Works when it closed.

A close-up of the tool holders, illustrating the complexity of the machines. *British Rail*

Pre-Assembly

Perhaps the most interesting work carried out at Redbridge was the preparation of complex rail layouts for the remodelling of track at places miles away from the depot. This not only involved bringing all the necessary materials together, laying them in pre-assembled form on a prepared piece of ground, (called the Fitting-up-Ground, the FUG), but it also required organising the loading of rail wagons with the components and sections so that they would be off-loaded at the scene of the work in the correct sequence and in manageable loads.

As we have seen, Redbridge actually manufactured the bulk items required; the sleepers, castings, and the rail switches and crossings. Only bolts and patent fittings were bought-in and this ability to bring all the locally produced products together into ready-to-lay track was one of the most satisfying features of the work carried out at Redbridge.

was to the usual 'V' or vertical format. It has been explained that all rails on straight track are inclined inwards at an angle of 20°. On a 'V' design a transition length is included on the approach to the points; and this is called the twist section in which the rail is brought from a 20° angle to vertical.

The drawing also gave the length, material and the positions of crossing timbers, the types of castings required between rails and sleepers, where joints were to be placed and the nature of the joint (i.e. open or insulating), the type of rail and the materials, (four steels; carbon, chrome, wear resistant 'B' and manganese were used until 1986 but from that time a wear resistant Grade A rail took the place of the first three types), and the position of closures, switch rails and stock rails, whether crossings were to be of cast manganese steel and all key dimensions and other relevant information including the requirements of the

A layout on Jarrah hardwood sleepers. The open-fronted switch assembly bay is to the right of the crane and the machine shops are behind.
John Fairman

Drawings for the manufacture of new points or more complex layouts were prepared by the Chief Civil Engineer's Department from site surveys and were dimensioned to fit accurately into the existing layout. Taking, as an example the relatively simple layout of type 'C' points illustrated. This was for Bishops Stortford in November, 1988. The drawing showed the type of turnout, (British Rail standard types A to G are of different lengths and radius of curve); and whether the design

signalling department, (i.e., the location of point motors). The engineer also had to remember that manganese steel could not be drilled 'on site', only in the workshops!

Materials listed were manufactured or drawn from stock and brought to the pre-assembly area, a perfectly flat part of the yard, for the engineer to position and to develop into the full-scale 'model' of the required layout. This called for considerable expertise and care and a logical approach was needed to build

Above: Assembling a diamond crossover, 7th August 1974 on Bob Reid's visit. Ivan Smith is alongside Sir Robert, Bill Pearson is doing the fitting work. Behind the concrete legs of the overhead crane gantry is the 5-ton derrick crane and far left one of the Jones diesel rail cranes that replaced the steam cranes.

Right: Examining an expansion joint made in the Works, left to right, Ivan Smith, (Works Manager), Robert Reid, Sid Elmes, (Machine Shop Assistant Foreman), and Mike Bidwell, (Production Manager).   *Both, British Rail*

the 'jig-saw'. Unfortunately, at Redbridge the yard was in the fresh air, easy for craneage but none too comfortable in the usual British weather!

The first step was to lay the timbers in order, numbered and with the correct spacing. (710mm is the distance between the centres of sleepers on straight track but this can vary on switches and crossings). The next step was to position the outer stock rail to form one of the straight lines from which cross measurements could be made. This was followed by longitudinal measurements from the first or lead(ing) rail of the points, to the length of switch or tongue rail, to the tip or nose of the crossing. Once in place these were temporarily bolted or clamped. Next, the rail off the back of the crossing was positioned and care taken to ensure a straight line, now extending over nearly 2/3 the length of the layout. Slides and base plates for these sections were then put into position and the accurate location of sleepers and castings marked with paint on the rails. For a crossover layout the next step was to measure and mark the nose to nose length of the crossings, then the dimension from the lead rail crossing to the other switch. Thus, step by step, gradually and methodically, a layout was built up, the gauge (1432mm for crossings), carefully checked for absolute accuracy, and the sleeper spacings and positions of chairs and bed plates established. Cork or resilient plastic pads or cushions had to be placed under

In August 1988, a diesel-electric crane, DRS 81336, built in 1962, was in use assembling a crossover layout for Bishops Stortford, in connection with the new branch to Stansted.

Centre left and below: The crossing timbers are numbered and the baseplates accurately positioned and screwed down.   *John Fairman*

Above: A 1934 layout of a 1 in 7 scissors crossover for the new Southampton Docks. In the background is the 1881 viaduct across the River Test.   *British Rail*

bedplates and chairs. Sleepers could be concrete or jarrah hardwood. Many recently constructed layouts had concrete; for example Brockenhurst, Poole, Rochester and Littlehampton.

Having completed the pre-assembly, and just prior to final inspection, one or two spikes were driven to locate each chair or bedplate casting at its exact position on the sleeper. Once the assembly was approved, the next step was to remove all rails including switches and crossings, and to load them in predetermined numbered sequence onto rail wagons for transport to the relaxing site. This left the sleepers and fastenings on the ground, still in their correct positions.

The final stage was to fit short, temporary, six to seven feet long, pieces of rail, butted tight, end to end, in the chairs and bedplates and to clip them in place. This, in effect gave a whole series of sections across the layout, each 6 to 7ft wide, again all carefully numbered in the correct sequence. The sections were then craned onto bogie wagons in bundles of two or three sleepers numbered on their ends for easy identification on site with reference to the drawing. Switch panels were usually on 9ft timbers for ease of transport.

The complexity of old type layouts can be seen from an early picture taken in 1926, of the re-arrangement of Cannon Street. Modern rationalised design and multiple unit electric or diesel rolling stock has considerably reduced the number of points and crossings required in a layout and has succeeded in its objective of cutting manufacturing and maintenance costs. All switches and crossings on the Southern are, in 1988, made from Grade A steel while non-magnetic cast-manganese or rolled-manganese rail is used for switch panels. Modern disc cutters and high-speed cobalt steel drills can be used successfully on the Grade A rail; essential tools in 'the field'. For electrified track sleepers have four holes at their outer ends for fixings for the third rail electrical insulators. These are now ETM 'positive' fixings on every sixth sleeper, instead of every fourth.

When visiting the railway look for other detailed aspects of track construction. Insulated block 'Edilon' joints for track circuiting were made in Redbridge machine shops using epoxy resin. Expansion joints were machined and may sometimes be found where long lengths of welded rail finish against sets of points. See if you can spot a twist section leading from the canted rail to a points made with vertical. The variety is fascinating!

Above: A charming picture of war effort in the Machine Shop, 1943.

Left: Brighton station layout, 5th March 1985. A good example of cast manganese steel crossings assembled in Redbridge yard.

Both, British Rail

45

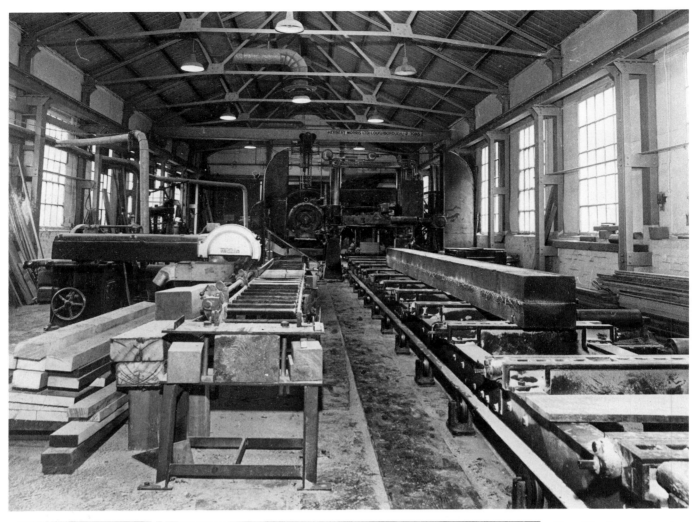

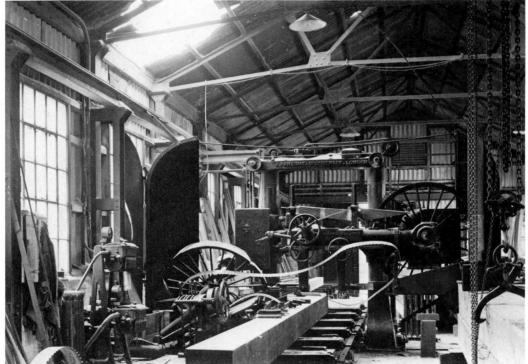

Above: View from north-eastern end of shop showing, left to right, trenching machine with rollerway for timber and moving table for old 1923 bandsaw.

Left: The bandsaw after an accident in 1948, showing the damage to the roof.

Jim Hodgson Collection

Sawmill

Timber handling, carpenters and shipwrights were traditional activities at Redbridge, long before railways arrived. Early plans of the site show a number of small sheds that were used when the wharf was a shipyard. William Sharland also carried on a timber merchant business at the yard before the L&SWR took over in 1879.

A railway sawmill was established at the Works soon after it was opened and the Linseed Oil and Oil-cake Mills building was adapted for that purpose when Dixon & Cardus moved out in the 1890's. A timber pond was also created by enclosing, with a series of posts and chains, an area of tidal mudland to the south

of the wharf. Rail siding access to the sawmill and to the northern edge of the pond was provided before 1895, so that wagons of timber could be taken for drying and then for cutting as required.

Heavy timber baulks and unsawn timber was unloaded at the wharf and often floated round to the pond in rafts, then moored with chains and left to season in the pond. It covered an area of about 5 acres and continued in use until the late 1960's.

The old sawmill and stores and the original building was demolished in 1924 and a new shed was built by the Southern Railway to house two principal machines; a Ransome & Pickles band saw, and a Pollard wood-boring machine. A separate shed

In the sawmill, (March 1979) are the 1923 Ransome and Pickles horizontal bandsaw and the feed runway for the table, the 2-tons overhead crane, the smaller pillar drill, right, and surface thickener and planer.
British Rail

Above: The sawmill, August 1988, showing the Stenner bandsaw installed in 1979 with its rollerway. The section of timber illustrates typical material used for bridge beams.

Left: Southampton, 22nd September 1988. This modern track layout, with manganese steel crossings, was pre-assembled at Redbridge on Jarrah sleepers and crossing timbers, using Pandrol fastenings. Notice that the crossovers are of different angles and will be subject to different speed restrictions.   *Both, John Fairman*

was provided for a cross-cut saw. Both buildings were on the south of the site, on the river frontage overlooking the timber pond. These machinists all had a remarkably long life and were still in use 54 years later! Near the sawmill, a timber drying shed was built where timber logs and baulks from the pond could be dried naturally by free circulation of air.

In 1965 the creosote works at Exmouth was closed and this released to Redbridge some additional machines; a circular rip-saw, a chain morticing machine, a planer and a single spindle moulding machine. These were all put to some use although the moulding machine served no purpose at a sawmill used generally for heavier work.

The production from the sawmill was varied in nature and size. Heavy bridge beams were regularly required to carry track on steel decked overbridges. Packers of all sizes were in constant demand, as well as materials for structures and fences. Chair keys, oak or teak were usually 'bought in' and did not form a part of the output from Redbridge. The level of activity in the mill tended to fluctuate and its use fell away towards the end of use of 'traditional' building construction materials.

Nevertheless a modest investment of £50,000 was made in 1979 when the old band-saw was pensioned off and replaced by a Stenner saw and a new roller track, a new Kitchen & Walker drill was installed and the overhead crane was renewed. At the same time, the heating, dust extraction and incineration plants were much improved. That essential annexe, the saw-doctor's shop adjoined the sawmill.

Reclamation

The recovery of cast iron chairs and fittings and the removal of these items from used sleepers may not have been the most glamorous activity at Redbridge but it was of considerable importance especially in the light of the need for good clean iron scrap to save buying pig-iron for the foundry cupolas.

Not all recovered chairs or sleepers were scrapped. Some were reusable on lighter duties, for example, in sidings but all the material returned from relaying work was examined and its fate decided at the reclamation yard.

It is reasonable to assume that the section had existed since sleepers were handled at the depot. Certainly the activity was well established in the 1920's, was particularly relevant in the last war, and was a busy unit, nearly to the end. From the 1940's and probably earlier, the reclamation dock occupied a part of the east end of the yard, south of the new foundry and north of that intriguing residence called 'The Bungalow'.

The platforms were made of typical Southern Railway pre-cast concrete construction, similar to a passenger station and they were wide enough for assembling and handling the sleepers and for the use of fork lift trucks. Used chaired sleepers from the District Engineer's Department were unloaded by the fork lifts and taken to the working area where there was an overhead electric hoist. The chaired sleepers were then put onto a roller track where a man graded the sleepers, for re-use or sale as scrap. Other men then removed the chairs by air-operated unscrewing machines. In the 1970's the reclamation section was manned to a level which could de-chair or de-baseplate about 1500 sleepers a week.

Most chairs, being obsolete, went to the foundry by this date but screw fastenings, if in sound condition, were returned for re-galvanising at 6p a time compared with a new screw at 28p.

Perhaps this chapter should close by mentioning the operational value of the large site for the many activities carried out at the depot. When it closed in 1989, it occupied an area of 42 acres and without congestion it had been able to carry out all the manufacturing work and accommodate the extensive stocks needed to carry out cost-effective operations. From an original area of 22 acres in 1925, with over 4 miles of sidings and a wharf

Men engaged in de-chairing sleepers. The man, second from left is using an air-operated unscrewing machine. The grader will decide on whether the sleeper is of any further use. The bins are for recovered screws and the wagon is for scrap chairs for the foundry. *Jim Hodgson Collection*

frontage of 900ft, it had grown to double the area under Southern Railway and British Railways management. The sidings had also nearly doubled in total length while the number of employees had remained about the same, 168 in 1936 and 166 in 1977. This near-constant level of manpower was attained although many major changes in production had taken place, as described in previous chapters. The numbers employed on building switches and crossings, and in the machine shops were up; the manning of the long welded rail section was an additional requirement while the labour for the handling and preparation of timber sleepers had disappeared.

By 22nd April 1988, the date the Works closing was announced, the number of staff employed was 127, listed by departments in Appendix 1. Truly, Redbridge Works had a long and fine history of achievement.

Right: More war effort! Emma Vine shows her strength by holding two chairs, each weighing over 40 lbs, 22nd February 1943.
British Rail

Below: Manpower at Redbridge 2nd November 1949. From left to right: Mr Knight, Jack Lee, John Diddams, Alf Holden, Stan Brixton, Jim Hodgson, Mr Wallace (from supplier of welding equipment), Mr Brown (from London Transport) and Mr Arundel. *Jim Hodgson Collection*

Motive Power

Undoubtedly horses were the first means of moving wagons in the yard but steam cranes were introduced at an early date. In December 1883 plans were approved for the erection of a new steam crane, the first of many.

Internal siding shunting appears to have been carried out by steam cranes for the 40 years Redbridge was a sleeper depot. Their ability to carry a slung load gave them a clear advantage compared with a locomotive. Main line engines were used for permanent way trains and shunted the sidings adjacent to the station.

In 1923/4 the additional wagon movements associated with the major reconstruction and building programme led to the arrival of a four coupled tank engine and a photograph on page eleven shows one of the B4 class at work near the wharf.

In 1927 it was decided to obtain a locomotive specifically allocated for the depot and in October a small 0-4-0T, was transferred to service stock as No. 77s. It had been built at Eastleigh Works as No. 745 in 1907 for light passenger train duties but much of its life had been spent shunting, especially at Southampton Town Quay. The old stone-built pump house near the west end of the works was adapted as an engine shed and was just long enough to accommodate the engine which measured 19ft 7in over its buffers. 77s was a familar sight puffing busily around the depot for over 30 years and, in locomotive terms was 'quite a character'.

Its reign at Redbridge ended in 1957 when it was needed for the Town Quay again in the years preceding dieselisation and after sporadic appearances at its old haunt, it was withdrawn from

Above: The 'C14' class 0-4-0T No. 77S, at the stone-built engine shed in February 1948. The shed was at the west end of the works by the river and it had once been a pump house for the chemical works.   *A.R. Sedgwick*

Left: A pre-war picture of No. 77S at Redbridge.
Lens of Sutton

service in 1959 and replaced by one of the larger 'O2' class 0-4-4T's from Eastleigh's allocation. Nos. 30212 and 30229 were examples of the class seen at Redbridge. Incidentally, they did not fit into the shed at all!

In October 1962, a trial was made with yet another class of shunting locomotive; a 1942 wartime USA-built 0-6-0T, No. 30061, one of 14 typical American switchers that had been purchased by the Southern Railway in 1947 for use in Southampton Docks. The 'Yankee' tank was successful and No. 30061 became service stock No. DS233. After a period of use at Meldon Quarry, it remained on Works duties for 4½ years until, in March, 1967, near the end of all Southern steam, it was replaced by one of the Drewry built 0-6-0 diesel shunters built in 1957. 11224 was an example. A Drewry was the usual class of shunter allocated by Eastleigh shed but if there was a shortage of drivers at Eastleigh, a Class 07, a 'Ruston & Hornsby', was borrowed, complete with driver from Southampton Docks. The local Drewry's were withdrawn by 1970 and 07's by 1977. The steam cranes also disappeared about 1970 and Engineer's Department diesel cranes were used for pre-assembly work up to Works closure. Since the 1970's one of Eastleigh's standard six-coupled 350hp diesel electric of Class 08 or 09 had been employed and as a tribute to the longest serving employee, William Pearson, a locomotive of this class was so-named on 3rd March 1989.

One final story. The locomotive shed came to an unhappy end one day in the late 1960's when it had its back wall demolished by the brake van of the 11.30 freight when it was accidentally shunted back into the shed!

Above: USA 0-6-0T, No. DS233, the second Redbridge Works shunter, on a visit to Eastleigh on 26th March 1966. DS233 spent over four years at the Works following a period of use at Meldon Quarry in Devon. It was displaced by a diesel shunter at the end of March 1967.
John Fairman

Below: Six coupled 204hp diesel-mechanical shunters made by Drewry replaced steam but Ruston and Hornsby 153hp diesel-hydraulic locomotives were sometimes borrowed from Southampton Docks. This 1967 picture shows one of the Docks locomotives shunting a train of LWR in the yard opposite Redbridge Jnc. and signalbox. Standard 350hp diesel-electric shunters from Eastleigh were employed from about 1970 on an 'as required' basis.
British Rail

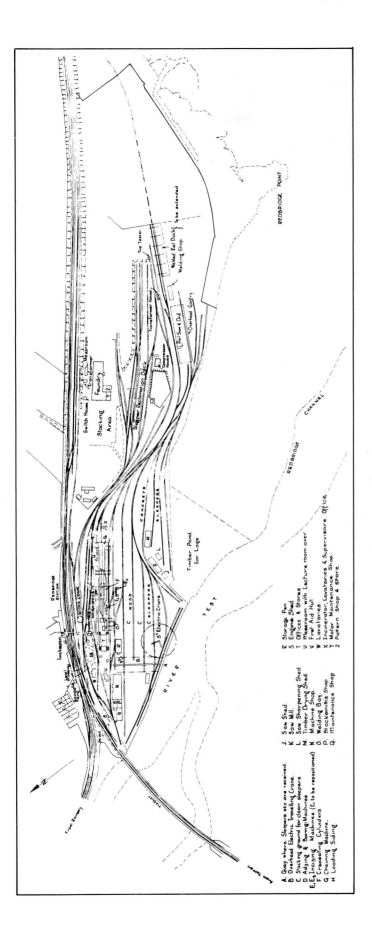

A. Quay where. Sleepers etc are received.
B. Overhead Electric Travelling Crane.
C. Stacking ground for clean sleepers
D. Adjsng & Boring Machines
E,E₁ Incising Machines. (E to be repositioned.)
F. Creosoting Cylinders
G. Cleaning Machine.
H. Loading Siding
J. Saw Shed
K. Saw Mill.
L. Saw Sharpening Shed
M. Timber Drying Shed
N. Machine Shop
O. Welding Bay
P. Blacksmiths Shop
Q. Maintenance Shop
R. Storage Pen
S. Engine Shed
T. Offices & Stores
U. Messroom with Lecture room over
W. First Aid Hut
X. Lavatories.
X₁ Incinerator, Lavatories & Supervisors Office
Y. Motor Maintenance.
Z. Pattern Shop & Store.

Redbridge Works, September 1962

This plan shows the completed development of the 1947-51 period, before the handling, storage, creosoting and chairing of wood sleepers had been discontinued. An area for storing and chairing concrete sleepers had been established near the timber pond but the extension of the flash-butt rail was only in the planning stage.

The characteristic view of Redbridge Works, May 1981, looking south-east from the station footbridge. The main line to Southampton is parallel with the left side of the picture. From left to right in the distance is the Foundry and the cupolas are at the right of the building. In the centre are the creosote storage tanks with their steam heaters. Behind the tanks, in the long shed are the pressure creosoting vessels and the wagon loading shed is at the left hand end. On the left of the tanks is the weighbridge. The group of three vertical tanks held fuel for the oil fired steam boilers. The heads of two cranes in the assembly yard can be seen over the rooftops.

British Rail

APPENDIX I

Development 1947 to 1951

Many of the changes made at the end of the war are mentioned in the book but notes made by Jim Hodgson, Assistant to the Works Manager, D. Slater, between 1946 and 1950, add to the information and are summarised below.

The production of chaired sleepers and switches and crossings from Redbridge was geared to a heavy programme of post-war track renewal. An early development was to pre-assemble 95 lb/yd rolled bull-head, chaired track inn 60ft lengths on timber sleepers, and lay it by crane. Early in 1946 a 7-mile length of the 'up' main line between Pirbright and Woking was laid with 113 lb/yd flat bottom section. In 1948, after Nationalisation, 109 lb/yd FB was adopted as standard with chairs replacing baseplates. In 1946, London Transport, at Lillie Bridge, pioneered work on flash-butt welding of 60ft into 300ft lengths. The Southern was impressed and decided to locate a welding plant at Redbridge.

Long welded track needed a stronger and heavier foundation and more robust sleepers. Pre-stressed concrete sleepers would replace the traditional creosoted timber and this dictated the re-development at Redbridge between 1947 and 1951.

In June 1947, Osmans, a Southampton contractor, started work on levelling a 30 acre site at the east of the old yard. On this area three activities were established. First, a reclamation section to systematise the recovery from old track of re-useable sleepers and fastenings; second a mechanised iron foundry to replace a life-expired manual plant and, thirdly, a flash-butt welding plant was built to produce 300ft rails. Unusually for such major works, most of the development was carried out by direct labour using Redbridge maintenance and building staff with specialist trade back-up from Eastleigh. The extensive additional sidings were laid on a 3ins carpet of Meldon screenings by a permanent way gang from the Division at Eastleigh.

The opening of the flash-butt welding plant on 2nd November 1949. Left to right: Chief Regional Officer, John Elliott; nearly hidden behind him is G.C. Stevens, Production Assistant, then Jim Hodgson, Mr Brown of London Transport, Douglas Slater the Works Manager and far right, V.A.M. Robertson, the Chief Civil Engineer. L.G.B. Rock, Permanent Way Assistant, is hidden from view.

APPENDIX II

Plant Inventory and Information 1947

Cranes: 5 ton electric travelling gantry crane on reinforced concrete gantry, 8hp derrick, 40hp hoisting, 15hp travelling and 8hp slewing motors.
Five steam travelling rail cranes. One, 7 tons, built 1894; one, 7 tons, built in 1904; one, 3 tons, built in 1881 and two, 3 tons, built in 1929.
One electric derrick crane, 5 tons capacity at 75ft radius, 2 tons at 96ft. Hoist motor 35hp and slewing, 10hp.

Electric Power Supply: Southampton Corporation, 6600v AC transformed to 440v, 50 cycles.

Yard Storage Capacity: 430,000 sleepers, 250,000 lin.ft. crossing timbers, 4000 tons chairs.

Sleeper Creosoting Plant: Two, each 75ft long, 7ft dia. Working pressure, 200 psi, 43 tons each empty, One charge, 464 sleepers 8ft 6ins x 10ins x 5ins. Supplied by Tinker, Shenton & Co., Hyde, Manchester. Two Armstrong Whitworth electric capstans, 28hp each, for 2ft 6ins gauge sleeper trolleys.
One 25hp electric 3-throw pump, Pearn & Co, Manchester. ¾hr under pressure.
One 27hp electric vacuum pump, Pearn & Co, Manchester. Three underground concrete storage tanks, No. 1, 40,000 galls, No. 2, 13,000 galls and No. 3, 40,000 galls. Creosote, 3 galls per sleeper.
One loco. type boiler, (1930), 160psi, 160°F.
Sleeper Adzing and Boring Machines. One by Ransome & Co. 1600 sleepers/day. 25hp, one by John Pickles Ltd. 2000 sleepers/day. Saws 9hp each, adzing 25hp and augers 12hp. Dust extraction plant, John Pickles Ltd.
Incising Machine. Robinson, Rochdale. 1600 sleepers/day. Max. size of logs incised, 70ft x 16ins x 16ins.
Ferruling Machine, Greenwood & Batley. 1600 sleepers/day. 10hp.

Chairing Machine and Elevator, Ransome & Co. 800 sleepers/day with 46lb chairs, 3 screws. 15hp.
Converted Chairing Machine and Elevator. Ransomes, converted by John Pickles and pressure plant by Drummonds. 1200/day with 46lb SI-X chairs, 2 through bolts. Two 7½hp spindle drives, 3hp feed drive, 3hp elevator drive, two 3hp pressure plant drives to create up to 10 tons pressure per chair.

Sawmill: All machinery by Ransome & Co. Log band saw, 50hp for logs up to 36 ins dia. x 50ft long, 12hp for feed drive. Circular saw, drag feed, 15hp. Wood borer, 3hp. General joiner, 7½hp. Cross-cut saw, (reciprocating), logs up to 48ins dia., 8hp. Production of timber about 83,000 cu.ft/annum. Log storage, 1500.

Foundry: Two 4-ton cupolas, one by Alldays & Onions, one made at Redbridge, 15hp fan. Hoist, 7½hp. Manual 30cwt traverser in shop. Continuous casting and sand reconditioning plant, knock-out grid, elevators to screen, screen, sandmill, five motors 15hp down to 1hp. Output 66½ tons castings/week.

Welding Shop: Quasi-Arc welding plant. Smithy: Two forges. Acetylene Welding and Cutting Plant: One 11hp electric hammer.

Machine Shop: Four J. Stirk & Sons rail planers, all with 60hp motors, split electric control and adjustable jigs: tables, 22ft x 5ft, 12ft x 5ft, 8ft x 5ft and 10ft x 4ft. One 6hp Clifton & Baird swivelling electric rail saw. Two 3ft 6ins Kitchen & Wade radial drilling machines. One Lang 8½ins lathe. One Campbell & Hunter shaping machine and other smaller machines.

Pattern Shop: 3hp, 30ins bandsaw, A. Ransome & Co. Saw grinding and sharpening equipment.

This view of Redbridge Junction on 28th April 1948 shows the level crossing at the entrance to the Works, also the locomotive shed on the left of the curve on the main line to Bournemouth. The line going right is to Romsey and Salisbury. The sidings on the right were provided when the line was opened from Andover via Romsey. In the centre background tipping has started to make the causeway for the widening of the road crossing of the River Test.

Jim Hodgson Collection

APPENDIX III

Staff Employed at Redbridge Works
22nd April 1988

Management 6
Supervisory 11
Technical Officers 4
Clerical Officers.. 13

Workshops
Machine Shop 31
Foundry... 30
Rail Welder 9
Sawmill 4
Reclamation.. 3
Ancilliary 6
Stores 16
Fitting-up Gang... 8
Maintenance 23

APPENDIX IV

Date	Stationmasters
1849-1863	A. Martin
1863/4	George Copus
1865-1880	Henry Sims
1881-1892	William Barnes
1893-1900	William Knight
1900/1	Arthur Binstead
1902/4	Edward Skilton
1905/7	Thomas Loveless
1908/10	Ernest Bench
1910-1923	Albert Laker
1923-1934	Herbert Gray
1934-1948	A.J. Smith
1948-1956	C. Dominey

Date	Works Superintendents (Residing at 'The Chestnuts')
1881-1893	Arthur Bailey
1893-1905	Mr McCarraher
191?-1923	Charles Pope
1923-1933	Harry Elsey
1933-1946	Thomas Haslett
1946-	Sydney Furnival
1947-	Reginald Restall

'The Chestnuts' ceased to be the home of the Superintendents about 1950.

Mr Slater was Works Engineer by 1950, Mr Baker in 1951 and Mr Ivan Smith to his sad death in 1987. At the close Mr L. Campuzano was Works Manager and Mr Mike Bidwell was the Production Manager.

APPENDIX V

List of 40 wagons at Redbridge for disposal, December 1988.

B457723. B461041
083163/71/97
083218/9
083345/82/3/4/6/7/8/90/8
083411/2/57/9/60/1/2/3/81/2
083532/3/5/6/8/9/40/2/3/4/5/7/53
083605

083345 was a Southern Railway bogie wagon, 083218 a five-plank open wagon, others were steel open wagons, formerly 'Medfits'.

Acknowledgements

The author is grateful for the willing assistance given by many people with information and photographs used in this book.

British Rail Engineering staff at Redbridge.
British Rail, Waterloo.

Hampshire County Record Office.
Southampton City Archivist and Librarian.
Public Records Office, Kew.

Local Newspaper files.
Local Directories.

Transaction of the Permanent Way Institution.

Modern British Permanent Way. C.J. Allen.
The Canals of Southern England. C. Hadfield.
The London & South Western Railway. R.A. Williams.
The Railway News. The Railway Magazine.